COASTAL FORCES

BRASSEY'S SEA POWER: Naval Vessels,
Weapons Systems and Technology Series:
Volume 10

Brassey's Sea Power:
Naval Vessels, Weapons Systems and Technology Series

General Editor: PROFESSOR G. TILL, Royal Naval College, Greenwich and
Department of War Studies, King's College
London

This series, consisting of twelve volumes, aims to explore the impact of modern technology on the shape, size and role of contemporary navies. Using case studies from around the world it explains the principles of naval operations and functions of naval vessels, aircraft and weapons systems. Each volume is written by an acknowledged expert in a clear, easy to understand style, and is well illustrated with photographs and diagrams. The series will be invaluable for naval officers under training and also will be of great interest to young professionals and naval enthusiasts.

COASTAL FORCES

by

BARRY CLARKE, JURGEN FIELITZ & MALCOLM TOUCHIN

With a Foreword by
Admiral Sir Julian Oswald GCB ADC
(Chief of British Naval Staff)

Edited by
Geoffrey Till

BRASSEY'S (UK)
LONDON * NEW YORK

Copyright © 1994 Brassey's (UK) Ltd.

First English edition 1994

UK editorial offices: Brassey's, 165 Great Dover Street, London SE1 4YA
orders: Marston Book Services, PO Box 87, Oxford OX2 ODT

USA orders: Macmillan Publishing Company, Front and Brown Streets, Riverside, NJ 08075

Distributed in North America to booksellers and wholesalers by the Macmillan Publishing Company, NY 10022

Library of Congress Cataloging in Publication Data
available

British Library Cataloging in Publication Data
A catalogue record for this book is
available from the British Library

0 08 040985 7 Hardcover
0 08 040986 5 Flexicover

Typeset by Florencetype Ltd, Kewstoke, Avon
Printed and bound in Great Britain by
Butler & Tanner Ltd, Frome and London

Cover photograph: HMS *Sandown* turning. (*Vosper Thorneycroft*)

Contents

Foreword

By Admiral Sir Julian Oswald GCB ADC
Chief of the Naval Staff (1989–93)

As the 1990s herald a new era of a single military Superpower, the focus of warfare at sea has shifted away from the open seas, blue water scenario of the Cold War. Now the risks are seen to come from emergent, regional powers seeking to exploit their newly-gained, high technology and capable weapons systems to pursue more localised interests. The maritime armed forces of many countries are therefore configured to operate close to land, either to pursue the ambitions of their governments, or to defend themselves against belligerent neighbours. Hence coastal waters are increasingly being seen as the maritime battlefield of the immediate future. Notwithstanding the risks of war between States and between ethnic communities within strife-torn States, those conducting activities such as piracy, the trade in drugs and arms, illegal immigration and other criminal acts frequently use the sea as their highway; the stakes are high and the Customs, Police and Armed Forces of nations affected are engaged in a relentless battle to control such activities, almost invariably in coastal waters.

Thus this latest volume in the Brassey's Sea Power series has an international relevancy today which far exceeds that envisaged only a few years ago. Professor Till has edited the work of three authors who are well qualified to write with authority on their particular subjects. While their words cannot be regarded as providing an official statement of policy, this book provides an important and very readable reference work in its field.

About the Authors

Barry Clarke
Barry Clarke's final appointment in the Royal Navy was as the Commodore Minor War Vessels where he commanded the Flotilla containing the Royal Navy's Mine Warfare and Offshore Patrol Vessels. From there he went to British Aerospace Defence, where he is Project Manager for the provision of mine-hunters, their support and training and their base facilities.

Barry Clarke wrote the section on Offshore Patrol Vessels.

Jurgen Fielitz
Jurgen Fielitz is currently a Commander in the German Navy serving as a staff officer operations at SHAPE Belgium. After serving on FPBs of different types and destroyers for several years he specialised in 1976 in naval operations and communications before commanding a *148 Type* FPB from 1977 to 1979 followed by two years as an Exercise Officer on a *143 Class* FPB. For another two years he served in the FPB flotilla as the communications staff officer.

Jurgen Fielitz wrote the section on Fast Patrol Boats.

Malcolm Touchin
Malcolm Touchin joined Ferranti Computer Systems Limited in Bracknell in 1978, where he was involved in the development of the operational software for the Royal Navy's *Hunt* class of MCMV. After some six years at Ferranti, he moved to CAP Scientific, now part of BAeSEMA, where he was closely involved with the development of the *NAUTIS-M* command system fitted to the Royal Navy's *Sandown* class Single Role Minehunters. He is currently working as a senior consultant across a wide spectrum of ship and submarine command system activities at BAeSEMA.

Malcolm Touchin wrote the section on Mine Warfare.

Geoffrey Till
Geoffrey Till is Professor of History and International Affairs at the Royal Naval College Greenwich and edited the volume.

Glossary

ARE	Admiralty Research Establishment
ARMS	Advanced Remote Minehunting System
ASMD	Anti-Ship Missile Defence
ASW	Anti-Submarine Warfare
C^2	Command and Control
CAAIS	Computer Assisted Action Information System
CAPTOR	Encapsulated Torpedo
CIS	Combined Influence Sweep
CMB	Coastal Motor Boat
COFAM	Computer Facility for Mine Warfare
COOP	Craft of Opportunity
CSP	Coastal Supply Point
DP	Dynamic Positioning
ECM	Electronic Countermeasure
EEZ	Exclusive Economic Zone
ESM	Electronic Support Measures
EW	Electronic Warfare
FAC	Fast Attack Craft
FPB	Fast Patrol Boat
FMDS	Floating Mine Disposal System
FSU	Forward Support Unit
GPS	Global Positioning System
GRP	Glass Reinforced Plastic
IR	Infra-Red
LOP	Line Of Position
LSL	Landing Ship Logistic
MASB	Motor Anti-Submarine Boats
MAS	Mine Avoiding Sonar

MCM	Mine Countermeasures
MCMV	Mine Countermeasures Vessel
MGB	Motor Gunboat
MHD	Minehunting Director
MP	Member of Parliament
MPA	Maritime Patrol Aircraft
MH	Maritime Headquarters
MSF	Minesweeper Fleet
MSSA	Minesweeping System Acoustic
MTB	Motor Torpedo Boat
MTSS	Minewarfare Tactical Support System
MWP	Mine Warfare Pilot
NAUTIS	Naval Autonomous Information System
NCGV	Norwegian Coast Guard Vessel
NOMBO	Non Mine Bottom Object
NTDS	Naval Tactical Data Systems
OPV	Offshore Patrol Vessel
PAP	*Poisson AutoProPulse*
PCC	Probability of Correct Classification
PCM	Position Control by Manoeuvre
PD	Probability of Detection
PDWS	Point Defence Weapons Systems
PINS	Precise Integrated Navigation System
RN	Royal Navy
RDN	Royal Danish Navy
ROV	Remotely Operated Vehicle
SAM	Surface to Air Missiles
SAR	Search and Rescue
SAV	Surface Auxiliary Vessel (for MCM)
SES	Surface Effect Ship
SRMH	Single Role Minehunter
SSM	Surface to Surface Missiles
SWATH	Small Waterplane Area Twin Hull
TPT	Third Party Targeting
UHF	Ultra High Frequency
USN	United States Navy
VEMS	Versatile Exercise Mine System
VHF	Very High Frequency
VMM	Variable Magnetic Moment

List of Figures

List of Plates

1

Maritime Operations in Coastal Waters

Most of the navies of the world are preoccupied with the need to exploit and protect local waters, rather than to undertake major bluewater operations in the open
ocean. This is partly because they do not have the financial or industrial resources
to aspire to such global operations.

THE PEACETIME IMPORTANCE OF COASTAL WATERS

With the reductions envisaged for the world's major navies in the wake of the ending of the Cold War, even they will find things more difficult in the future than
they have been in the past. But there is another reason for the preoccupation with
local waters as well, and that is the growing public and commercial importance of
the offshore estate. This has a number of causes:

▶ Marine resources, including coal, oil and gas as well as living resources
have become critical elements in the world economy.

▶ The security of harbours, harbour approaches and shipping routes in
coastal and restricted seas is essential for the efficient working of the international trading system on which the prosperity and stability of the world
depend.

▶ In an era in which drugs have become the most valuable single com-
modity traded internationally, and the abuse of which threatens the fabric of
producer and consumer states alike, anti-drug smuggling operations have
become increasingly important. Other commodities continue to be smuggled
as well.

▶ Although Maritime terrorism against ships and oil rigs has not in fact
expanded at the rate expected in some quarters a few years ago, guarding
against it remains an important concern. Many states also need to prevent
gun-running and other types of subversive activity in their local waters.

▶ llegal immigration has become a worry to many countries especially in
the more developed parts of the world. The Vietnamese boat people,
Chinese immigration to Hong Kong, Albanian refugees fleeing to Italy are
only some of the most obvious recent examples. The countries of Southern

PLATE 1.1   A US Coastguard 33 m patrol craft (*Photo: Vosper Thorneycroft*)

PLATE 1.2 The Gambian Navy's Fairey Marine *Tracker 2* class of Coastal Patrol Craft. Of 34 tons, it is armed with one 20mm gun. (*Photo: Eric Grove*)

PLATE 1.3 Fairey Marine also built this 17 ton *Lance* class Coastal Patrol craft for the Gambian Navy. (*Photo: Eric Grove*)

Europe, in particular, have become increasingly concerned about the prospect of large scale and illicit population movements northwards from the Maghreb.

▶ Piracy, far from being stamped out, appears in some parts of the world (most notably West Africa and South East Asia) to be increasing, and has to be controlled.

▶ With more international concern for environmental matters, there has been a growth of interest in associated maritime activities. Oil pollution has been a concern of coastal states for many years, but such anxieties have been reinforced by the appalling images of environmental destruction that appeared during the Gulf War of 1991. Not surprisingly, more and more countries are considering ways to increase the extent to which they can regulate their offshore waters against pollution, looting and general misuse.

These economic and social concerns have contributed to what some experts have called the 'creeping jurisdiction' on coastal waters. With the completion of the United Nations Conference on the Law of the Sea in 1981, territorial seas are now generally recognised to have extended from 3 to 12 miles, and littoral states have won increased rights to supervise and exploit an economic zone extending out to 200 miles from their coastline. These legal changes simply reflect the growth in importance of coastal seas and are designed to protect the capacity of littoral states to exploit and protect them.

The need to supervise and defend coastal waters has led to the creation around the world of countless maritime forces dedicated to the task. Of these probably the most famous is the US Coastguard, which has a tonnage and military capacity superior to most of the world's navies. The US Coastguard comprises nearly 40,000 officers and men who operate about 50 cutters (some of which are of more than 3000 tons displacement) 80 patrol craft and a host of other auxiliary vessels of one sort or another. At the other end of the scale, perhaps, comes the diminutive navy of the Gambia, able to operate no more than a handful of small coastal patrol craft.

A more typical model than either of these is the Norwegian Coastguard. Part of the Royal Norwegian Navy, its 13 vessels are divided into two squadrons responsible for the Northern and Southern parts of the country. They have an extensive area to cover, namely the Exclusive Economic Zone (EEZ), the fishery protection zone around Svalbard and the fishery zone around the island of Jan Mayen which adds up to an area of approximately 2.24 million square kilometres. The length of the coastline totals some 21,200 kilometres and includes 150,000 islands. The Coastguard understands its role to be:

▶ General surveillance and supervision in the Norwegian Economic Zone and the continental shelf, in the Svalbard fishery protection zone and the fishery zone around Jan Mayen.

▶ Surveillance of fishery borders, trawl-free zones, gear protection and auxiliary services for Norwegian fishermen at sea. In 1991, the Coastguard

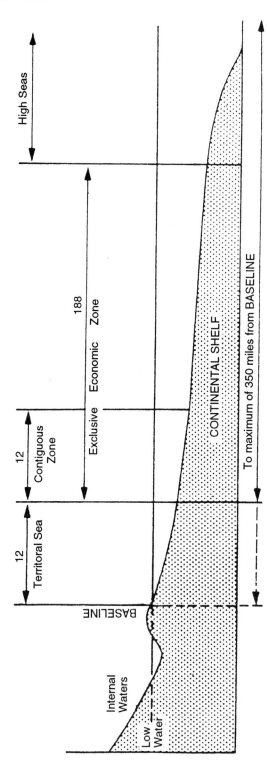

Fig. 1.1   Zones Permitted Under the 1982 UN Convention on the Law of the Sea (The Montego Bay Convention)

PLATE 1.4   The *Nordkapp* class CVG *Andenes* on patrol near off-shore installations in the North Sea. This class is designed to control emergency operations through extensive command, control and information facilities. (*Photo: Royal Norwegian Navy*)

PLATE 1.5   Frigates like the Royal Norwegian Navy's 1450 ton *Oslo* class can have an important role to play in offshore waters for a coastal navy. (*Photo: Royal Norwegian Navy*)

PLATE 1.6   Some see a progression towards the corvette type of offshore patrol vessel like the 780 ton *Sleipner* of the Royal Norwegian Navy. (*Photo: Royal Norwegian Navy*)

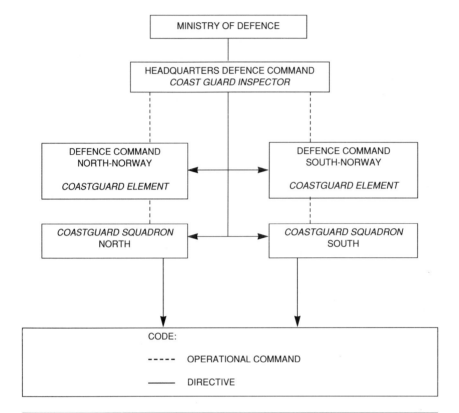

ORGANIZATION

OF

THE NORWEGIAN COASTGUARD

In the choice of an organizational structure for the Coastguard service, importance was attached to:
- The need for rapid expansion of the new national services
- The clearest possible division of responsibility
- Maximal utilization of already existing personnel
- Maximal utilization of already existing national material, bases and other installations
- Coordination of the fisheries surveillance service monitoring duties on the continental shelf

FIG. 1.2   Organisation of the Norwegian Coastguard

PLATE 1.7   Coastal submarines like the Norwegian *Type 207 Skinna* are an important part of a coastal navy and can be very difficult for large outsiders to deal with.
(Photo: Royal Norwegian Navy)

PLATE 1.8   The typical craft of the advanced coastal navy, the 125 ton *Skudd*
missile-armed Fast Patrol Boat. *(Photo: Royal Norwegian Navy)*

PLATE 1.9   The *Vidar* one of the Royal Norwegian Navy's coastal minelayers.
(Photo: Royal Norwegian Navy)

carried out 2449 inspections of fishing vessels, issued 498 warnings and made 70 arrests.

▶   Ensuring that no unauthorised scientific research is carried out on the Norwegian continental shelf.

▶   Search and rescue.

▶   Cleaning-up oil spills, research assistance and help to other Government agencies.

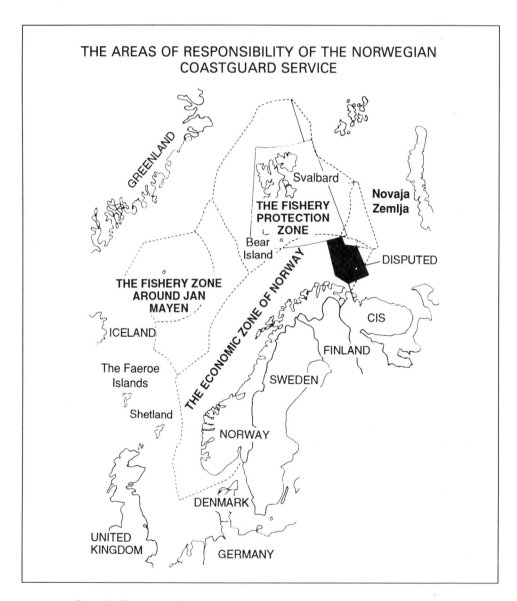

FIG. 1.3   The Areas of Responsibility of the Norwegian Coastguard Service

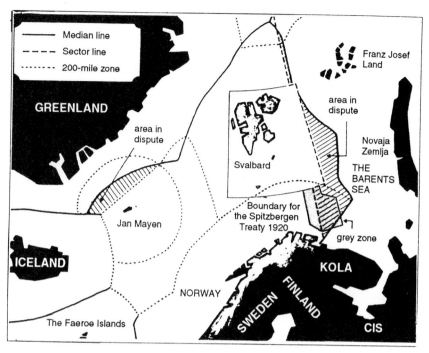

FIG. 1.4   Complexities and Disputes
Although with the ending of the Cold War Europe's northern waters are much less
sensitive strategically, there remain a number of jurisdictional disputes between
Norway and its neighbours. Norwegian rights have frequently to be upheld by the
Coastguard

Some of the Coastguard's activities can be dramatic, such as in 1989 when a
Coastguard vessel, *Senia* rescued nearly 700 passengers and crew from the Soviet
cruise liner *Maxim Gorky* when it hit heavy ice near the Spitsbergen archipelago.
In 1991, more typically, Coastguard vessels carried out about 500 support tasks,
ranging from helicopter medevac, search and rescue (SAR), to icebreaking.

In wartime, the Coastguard would have a variety of military functions. Indeed
the 3240 ton Nordkapp-class vessel NCGV *Andenes* was the Norwegian naval
contribution to UN operations in the Gulf in 1990–1.

THE MILITARY IMPORTANCE OF COASTAL WATERS

But these are the offshore concerns of peacetime. Local waters are important
for military and strategic reasons too. Indeed it is often forgotten that the great
majority of the world's most famous naval battles have been fought within 60
miles of the coastline. Naval warfare is more typical of coastal waters than it is of
the open ocean, and the Gulf War of 1991 provided many examples of the forms
such operations can take.

Operations in the Gulf, 1991

The maritime side of the Gulf war took place in the restricted waters typical of coastal operations and forces. The Gulf is long and thin, entered by a narrow choke point, has much shallow water unsuitable for ocean-going warships and is almost entirely surrounded by land and shore-based missiles and aircraft. The Red Sea, where operations were also conducted, is almost as bad. It is an area that is ideally suited to coastal forces such as those described in this book.

But what the war in fact showed was that the difference between coastal and bluewater operations was one of scale, not of kind. Before hostilities began, there were many who argued that it would be impossible for the US Navy's Carrier Battle groups to operate within such restricted waters. They would be too vulnerable to mines and shore-based aircraft and missiles and would not be able to find the sea room necessary for dispersion and manoeuvre. In the event four such battle groups operated in the Gulf simultaneously (namely those of the USS *Midway*, *Ranger*, *America* and *Theodore Roosevelt*) with another two in the Red Sea. Moreover, many of the tasks associated with coastal operations were in fact conducted by ocean-going warships.

On the other hand, there was no doubt that the strategic consequence of such coastal operations could easily become global in scale, especially where they had an impact upon the vital oil trade. The arrival of Minesweepers and Minehunters from Europe and the United States (whether they made their way to the Gulf independently, or via a transport dock in the case of the US vessels) showed that small vessels designed for coastal operations could in fact have a global reach.

Coastal operations, and many of the forces designed to conduct them, should not therefore be thought wholly distinct from those of the open oceans. On the contrary, they share many problems, characteristics and preoccupations. The differences are of degree not of kind.

The Gulf: Coastal patrol and supervision Coastal patrol in the Gulf crisis and war was dominated by the massive international maritime blockade conducted in support of UN sanctions, but was largely carried out by the ocean-going warships of the Coalition. Over a 10-month period, more that 165 ships from 14 Allied nations challenged more than 10,000 merchant vessels and boarded about 1500 to inspect manifests and cargo holds. The boardings were usually from small boats and helicopters, and in the US case were often conducted by Coastguard detachments familiar with the legal niceties of the situation.

Diverted ships needed to be escorted to directed ports and closely monitored lest they sought to release oil or cause an incident of some sort. Coordinating and controlling this vast global effort required much liaison with the commercial world and took a good deal of communications engineering. The operation continued long after the war was finished.

The war led to an unprecedented degree of environmental vandalism on the part of Iraq and much of this had severe consequences for the marine ecology. As soon as it was safe to do so, large numbers of small vessels were enlisted to clean away the oil pollution, and to remove as much as was practicable of the destructive detritus of war. Coastal forces were and will continue to be essential if the Gulf states wish to see their waters returning to normal after the last tragic decade or so.

Once hostilities began, Iraqi-controlled islands and offshore oil rigs became the target of coalition attack partly for their value in sustaining Iraq's war economy and partly because they were useful to the Iraqis for intelligence purposes and as a base for possible operations.

Fast patrol boats in the Gulf war When the Gulf war began, the Iraqis had about 80 small combatants of various sorts and had taken over a number of small Kuwaiti vessels as well. The 8 ex-Kuwaiti *TNC-45s* carried *Exocet*, and a number of the ex-Russian Iraqi FPBs were equipped with *Styx* missiles. It was the conventional wisdom that FPBs armed with surface-to-surface missiles could in some circumstances be regarded as a potent threat to much larger bluewater forces, and should therefore be treated with some circumspection. Indeed, in some circles it was argued that this combination of weapon and platform could well narrow the gap between the great navies and the small ones, especially in restricted waters like the Gulf.

In point of fact, no such threat materialised. Iraqi coastal forces *were* used but apparently not against Coalition forces at sea. There were no FPB *versus* FPB battles either. Instead Iraqi coastal forces laid minefields, ran supplies to offshore islands, tried to move troops along the coast in support of the Khafji operation, moved out to sea in order to escape from ports subject to heavy air-raids, and finally sought simply to find sanctuary in Iranian waters.

Despite their cautious use, about half these FPBs were sunk and the remainder were disabled. The principal anti-FPB platform turned out to be helicopters operating from ships. 3 British *Lynx* helicopters operating from HM Ships *Cardiff*, *Gloucester* and *Manchester* disabled 15 of these small combatants with 26 *Sea Skua* missiles. These small missiles had a range of about 8 miles, a warhead of 44 lbs and proved effective against soft-skinned targets like minelayers and fast patrol craft. They were often guided to their targets by American *SH–90* helicopters which had good sensors but no anti-FPB missiles. (Norwegian *Penguins* had been ordered but were not deployed). The Royal Saudi Navy's *Dauphin* helicopters armed with the *Aerospatiale AS 15TT* missile were also used effectively in this role, disabling 5 vessels with 15 missiles.

The helicopters found that the range of their missiles allowed them to fire with impunity from outside the target's defensive envelope. Sometimes the missiles missed because the targets were too low in the water. The hitting power of the missiles was usually too limited actually to sink the target. In many cases, though, these small ships were finished off by fixed-wing aircraft with bombs and rockets. The US Navy's *A-6E Intruders* and *F/A 18 Hornets* used *Harpoon* missiles and *Skipper* and *Rockeye* bombs. The RAF *Jaguars* used *CRV 7* rockets.

All in all, the FPB threat to bluewater forces failed to materialise, and the critical thing in this case appears to have been the Coalition's high degree of air superiority which allowed its helicopters to perform their tasks in relative safety. Had the Coalition found it necessary seriously to defend its naval forces from air attack, then it might have been a different story. Some have argued that the Gulf experience confirms the need for larger and more capable FPBs, perhaps approaching the size of Corvettes, which would have space for better defensive sensors and weapons.

Mine warfare in the Gulf At the beginning of the war, Iraqi mine stocks were considerable. While many of their mines were Soviet *Krabs*, *MO8* and *MKB* mines of ancient design and provenance, others were advanced and posed quite a challenge. The Italian *MISAR* mine for instance was an influence bottom mine, that could be laid to 100 metres, had a 140 kg warhead and was plastic-cased and therefore difficult to detect. The variety of mines was a problem too, with the Iraqis cannibalising their stocks to produce unexpected combinations. The Iraqis had several hundred minelayers, including helicopters, *Badger* and *Blinder* aircraft, *Polnochny* amphibious warfare ships, a variety of minewarfare ships, air cushion vehicles and, potentially, a large number of trawlers and merchant ships.

In the event, the Iraqis laid some 1200 mines off Kuwait, and more on the beaches themselves. The sea mines were deployed in 6 fields in a 150 mile arc from Faylaka Island, down to the Saudi–Kuwaiti border, with an additional 4 mine lines behind the arc. Another hazard was floating mines which were either illegally released as such, or which broke free from their moorings because they had not been laid properly.

Quite clearly, Coalition naval forces would have to clear these mines, wholly or partly. The floating mines represented a serious hazard to general shipping in the area. Naval gunfire support had an important role to play in attacking Iraqi positions ashore and in strengthening the Iraqi fear that an amphibious assault was imminent. The bombarding battleships therefore needed approach routes and a large fire support area cleared for them. Should the threatened amphibious assault eventually have gone ahead, it would have been necessary to sweep the beach approaches, and clear the landing area.

The need for such caution was demonstrated on 18 February when the helicopter carrier *USS Tripoli* and the *Aegis* class cruiser *USS Princeton* both sustained severe mine damage. The dilemma was reminiscent of the Dardanelles in 1915. Before the big ships could go in, the MCM force would need to clear the way for them. But this would require them to operate close to a hostile shore, and here they would need to be protected themselves. In 1991, organic air power provided much of the protection missed in 1915, but even so there were problems similar to those of that period. For example, to protect the MCM force from a possible Iraqi shore-based *Silkworm* missile attack, *USS Princeton* needed to move into an area that had not been fully cleared: it was then that the mines struck. The stern of the ship was lifted 10 feet out of the water, causing severe whiplash and a cycle of vertical and lateral shock waves. Half the ship's power plant was disabled, the hull was severely distorted, the keel strained and the quarterdeck buckled. Aft gun and missile systems were put out of action. The ship remained on station until relieved and then departed for repairs at Dubai before returning to the United States. Had it not been for prompt and effective damage control, things could have been considerably worse.

This experience demonstrated the continuing cost-effectiveness of minewarfare. The presence of the mines greatly complicated the Coalition's operational planning and would have made large-scale amphibious landings more hazardous. The damage inflicted on the two ships struck was significant, both in terms of operational effectiveness and in terms of cost of repair. Even with the aid of Iraqi plans of the minefields, clearing them has proved a long and laborious task, that has continued long after hostilities ceased.

The clearance task has been performed by an international minesweeping force, before, during and after the war. The British contribution centred on the 5 *Hunt* class MCM ships, HM Ships *Hurworth, Cattistock, Atherstone, Ledbury* and *Dulverton*. These vessels are constructed of glass-reinforced plastic, weigh 700 tonnes and carry a crew of 45. Their engines are mounted on rubber and their equipment is designed to emit only very low magnetic signals. They were designed to operate only for short periods but with the aid of the survey ships HMS *Herald* and *Hecla* which acted as MCM Command and support ships, and the LSL *Sir Galahad* which provided fuel, water and so forth, they were able to operate continuously for weeks on end. To monitor the magnetic and acoustic signatures of the MCM ships regularly, transportable Degaussing and Organic ranges were operated at Dubai and Bahrain. After nearly 10 years of continuous operation in the Gulf, the British were familiar with local conditions and this proved to be of a great advantage.

Needing to operate so close to occupied Kuwait (at the end of the war, to within 8 miles of the coast) the defences of the MCM ships were strengthened with 2 × 20mm BMARC cannon, chaff dispensers, electronic support measures of various kinds and chemical detectors. Since the MCM force was obviously unable to rely on radio fixing aid coverage, satellite links were enhanced with *GPS NAVSTAR XR4* receivers to help provide the navigational accuracy so necessary for mine clearance. During these operations the British developed the Floating Mine Disposal System Mk 1 (FMDS) to cope with this especially difficult problem. Mines moored near the surface posed a particular threat to the MCM ships themselves, and *Mine Avoidance Sonar* (MAS) was developed to help counter it. This simply diverted the sonar beam from the sea-bed, sideways into the surface layer. The helicopter-operated *Demon* camera also proved effective in this role.

The American mine clearance effort was substantial, during and after hostilities. It centred on the 6 *MH-53E Sea Stallion* helicopter sweepers embarked on *USS Tripoli*, the old wooden minesweepers *USS Adroit, Impervious* and *Leader* (all of which date from the mid 1950s) and the brand new *USS Avenger*. The older US MCM ships were taken to the Gulf by the Dutch Transport dock *Sea Servant III*, an interesting way of giving coastal forces strategic mobility.

The *USS Avenger* developed engine trouble and the extent of American dependence on British and other foreign expertise in the humdrum but essential business of mine clearance has attracted much comment. Italian, Belgian Dutch, Norwegian and, significantly, German and Japanese MCM squadrons all arrived in the Gulf too and were soon busy at work clearing the mines once hostilities were over. It will probably be years before the last mine is disposed of, however. Now, all such forces are engaged in the routine but demanding work of route survey, harbour and approach clearance of the sort described later in this book.

The Gulf War: Matters Arising

This survey of the forces engaged in coastal operations before, during and after the Gulf war of 1991, raises more questions than it answers. But one thing did become clear, and this was the general importance of the control of coastal waters. This conflict, and the long run-up to it, provided dramatic examples of the kind of coastal operations that take place in times of peace, tension and war everywhere and all the time. Amongst the reasons for this is the fact, as one of the last books produced by the thinkers of the Soviet Navy reminded us, that the military-economic potential of coastal waters can now be so great that their defence and attack might be of crucial significance to the outcome of war.[1]

Gulf operations also indicate the huge variety of the forms that coastal operations can take, and therefore the wide range of military operations that coastal navies may well need to prepare for. The complexity and variety of the coastal task is often underestimated by those preoccupied with events on the high seas.

A brief description of a fairly typical coastal navy, such as that of Norway, perhaps makes the point most clearly. As we have already seen, the Royal Norwegian Navy has a very large area to cover. It comprises ships up to frigate size and has to operate in difficult sea areas, in order to maintain surveillance and protect coastal sea lines of communication.

Like a large number of countries around the world, it puts much emphasis on the maintenance of a surprisingly large fleet of specialist coastal submarines, which, together with its FPB forces are specially trained to make the most of the unique topographical conditions presented by Norway's extensive coastline. Mine warfare is of obvious importance in such an environment. Finally, the Royal Norwegian Navy is backed up by an extensive Coastal Artillery force whose function is to defend against sea-borne invasion and attack by the operation of guns, shore-based torpedoes and controlled minefields.

The Royal Norwegian Navy may be small, but its tasks are neither negligible nor simple. It provides us with a useful reminder of the need to take coastal forces and operations seriously.

But to return to matters arising from the Gulf war, there are many narrower technical and tactical questions as well. For instance, to what extent were these operations typical? Were there any surprises? What lessons will the world's navies deduce from this experience in their future planning?

At first glance it would seem that there is likely to be increased interest in any system which offers FPBs protection from helicopters with air to surface missiles. The proven utility of the helicopter might tempt more navies into developing corvettes with the ability to operate them. Perhaps, this will encourage a move towards larger multipurpose OPVs able to combine several of the separate functions of coastal operations more easily.

In some quarters, it was argued that the Gulf war has finally destroyed the myth created by the fate of the Israeli destroyer *Eilat* in 1967 that large ships were prohibitively vulnerable to FPBs armed with surface-to-surface missiles. But we must ask ourselves, would it be safe to assume in any future operation that big ships would be as safe against such attack as they turned out to be in 1991, especially if the degree of air superiority was less absolute?

Of course, some large ships *were* damaged – by mines. It is sometimes forgotten that mines sank more shipping in the Second World War than any other weapon: the Gulf war demonstrated once more how cost-effective this weapon can be, and how important it is to continue to invest in mine warfare.

In order to explore such issues further, we will need to investigate the nature of coastal operations and the forces that normally perform them in much more detail. We will turn, in the next chapter, to the business of Offshore Patrol.

2
Offshore Patrol: An Introduction

Offshore patrol is one of many warfare skills that make up the fabric of maritime warfare. It is a specialised area away from the mainstream of naval operations, having a peacetime task equal to that of war. It is conducted in the 'offshore tapestry', which is that area of water stretching out to a boundary defined by the requirement of a nation to control its interests.

Mention of Coastal Warfare evokes Second World War films of FPBs speeding across calm seas against a background of the white cliffs of Dover, intent on meeting E Boats off the enemy coast or slipping in under cover of darkness to land agents on foreign soil. Times have changed. For many years now it has been envisaged that the real war at sea will be fought at long range, probably well away from coasts and in the 'blue waters'. With the technology of blue water warfare moving forward swiftly, the demands placed on the larger navies to retain their fighting capability has left little funding for what are seen as lower priority tasks. FPBs have therefore gone from the fleet lists of the larger navies. An attempt to redress this omission by placing the NATO requirement for FPBs on the smaller European NATO navies has resulted in the skills of FPB Coastal Warfare now being the preserve of countries such as Norway, Denmark and West Germany. This is particularly true of Norway, where the fjords provide waters in which the skills of lying up, under camouflage in the corner of a fjord, and using local knowledge to speed through small gaps to attack the enemy, have been perfected. But this is the glamorous aspect of coastal warfare. The real work is done in a host of other areas vitally important to the protection of the offshore tapestry. This work requires minesweepers, minehunters and offshore patrol vessels (OPV). These are now the main naval inhabitants of the offshore waters of many nations.

As we saw in Chapter 1, Coastal Warfare includes a range of separate subjects which are areas of warfare in their own right. Setting aside the role of the FPB, these are mainly defensive in character, ranging through mine warfare, surveillance and marking of suspicious or potential enemy vessels, coastal convoy routing and protection, the Examination Service, the defence of ports and anchorages, coastal surveying, the defence of offshore oil and gas rigs, fishery protection and anti-smuggling, particularly in the drug enforcement area. All require some form of offshore patrol. The aim of this chapter and those which follow is to concentrate on offshore patrol without straying too far into mine warfare, fishery protection or FPBs, which form integral parts of the offshore scene but are the subjects of other chapters.

HISTORICAL EXPERIENCE. CLASHES AND CHOICES

Offshore patrol was one of the early tasks given to navies. In the late sixteenth century there was an English squadron operating from Lowestoft with a primary aim of fishery protection. Offshore patrol is not always performed off one's own coast. Nelson used coastal vessels to patrol off enemy ports to give warning of their fleet's departure from port. In the first half of the twentieth century, the Royal Navy used shallow draft patrol vessels, such as HMS *Ladybird*, to patrol the wide stretches of the Yangtse River on the China Station. The *Ladybird* was eventually sunk off the North African Coast in the Second World War. After that war, the Royal Navy reverted to the more traditional economy measure of using warships designed for blue water warfare for offshore patrol tasks. Hence we saw the frigate HMS *Amethyst* in what came to be known as the 'Yangtse Incident' and frigates used in such tasks as the Cyprus patrol and the patrol of coastal waters between the Bahamas and Cuba in the fifties and sixties.

An economy measure in the fifties led to the Royal Navy building a class of smaller, cheap frigates of the *Type 14* class, labelled Second Rate frigates and intended for warfare in the offshore waters. However, although some were employed on distant water fishery protection, they proved capable of Fleet training and ocean tasks and were pressed into general service with the Fleet, so keeping up the numbers of frigates that were allocated to NATO ocean exercises.

Whilst the smaller minesweepers of the *Ton* class were used in coastal waters of the United Kingdom, the Gulf, the Malacca Straits and Hong Kong, frigates were used in the sixties and seventies for the patrol off Beira, in the West Indies and for the Royal Navy's fishery protection role off the coasts of Iceland, Greenland and North Norway. This led to front line modern frigates being used as offshore patrol vessels in the 'Cod War' of the seventies, where their blue water armament and slender skins were unsuitable for the task of countering the tactics of the tough, purpose built offshore patrol vessels of the Icelandic Coastguard. However, with the help of funding from the Ministry of Agriculture, Fisheries and Food, the Royal Navy produced a purpose built class of offshore patrol vessels in the seventies, named the *Island* class. The two vessels of the subsequent *Castle* class were used in the Falklands War and one remains permanently on patrol in Falklands offshore waters.

We have dwelt on the thread of Royal Navy experience of warships for offshore patrol to draw a few lessons. With a Navy oriented towards a worldwide task and blue water warfare, it is tempting, when economy bites, to avoid the expense of purpose built offshore vessels by pressing older, or sometimes not so old, blue water ships into offshore tasks. This was done in the late nineteenth century when a small cruiser and some ocean minesweepers came together to start the present Fishery Protection Squadron.

Experience since the Second World War has shown that use of blue water warships for offshore patrol can be a less efficient, less capable and less economical path to follow. Hence the present make up of the Fishery Protection Squadron is of largely purpose built ships. However, no lesson is really learnt. Recently, the proposed *OPV3* class, (to follow on after the *Castle* class) was designed with all the experience of the former two classes of offshore patrol vessels in mind. It would have been more capable of undertaking the offshore task, but more expensive. The result was a design that came to be seen as a threat to funding necessary for blue water frigates. The eventual decision was to concentrate available funding on those Front Line frigates. The circle was completed.

The future for offshore patrol for the Royal Navy therefore looks like a choice between very sophisticated *Type 22* or *23* frigates or slow *Hunt* or *Sandown* class minehunters which are on the small side for true offshore work. But the Royal Navy is not alone in these compromise measures. Canada uses frigates for patrol of the Grand Banks fishing grounds and the Royal Netherlands Navy patrols its area of the North Sea with them.

In contrast, it is worth looking at organisations which are devoted solely to the offshore patrol task, the most well known being the US Coastguard. As a separate service, but under the wing of the USN, it has mostly stayed with its own designs of vessels for offshore work. These, whilst on some occasions acknowledging USN influence, have proved to be robust designs capable of performing their tasks inshore and offshore in an economic manner. The professional US Coastguarder is unlikely to accept that a modern Naval frigate and her Navy men could replace the vessels, the expertise and the experience of the offshore scene that the US Coastguard exercises.

Although the Royal Navy has, for the present, turned its back on acquiring a new class of offshore patrol vessels, British shipyards have developed designs for export. The Brunei requirement, for example, has produced some interesting developments leading to what, in British terms, are third generation offshore patrol vessel designs.

The People in Offshore Patrol The drafting of naval personnel moves men from one ship type to another. However, on average, the personnel in offshore patrol vessels are a different breed from those in frigates and destroyers. Those men who volunteer to return again to an offshore patrol vessel are not warfare computer experts, but more natural seamen who like being closer to the sea. They enjoy the smaller community and hence more informal method of working that these ships have. A smaller ship's company leads to them having greater responsibility placed on them than the equivalent in a larger ship. Each must be ready to do a wider range of jobs, the steward being the coxswain of the inflatable craft or the stores assistant watchkeeping on the Bridge.

For the small group of officers onboard, offshore patrol vessels are an ideal training ground. Most of them, including the First Lieutenant, are in the earlier stages of their naval careers but have much responsibility for their crew and the activity of the ship. For the young Commanding Officers there is not only the challenge of responsibility for their ship, but by the nature of their task, offshore patrol vessels operate alone. This leaves the Commanding Officer with many more occasions when there is the need for independent decision making than would be expected in bigger warships.

Because offshore patrol vessels are relatively simple to maintain, they spend a greater proportion of their time at sea. Accommodation onboard is therefore planned more generously than that in bigger ships. This is possible because the relatively small weapon outfit in an Offshore Patrol Vessel does not put the same pressure for space on the design.

All of those onboard these smaller ships, must be happy in the lively motion of an offshore patrol vessel operating well to seaward in exposed waters. With a small crew there is no room for seasickness that prevents personnel doing their job. The typical crew is therefore closely united with each member pulling their own weight. Crew are fit, ready to accept responsibility, understand the sea, support their young officers and have a fierce loyalty for their ship. However, they are unlikely to be good in a billet in the sophisticated operations room of a modern frigate or destroyer.

3

Offshore Patrol in Peacetime

Until economics became an important part in determining the influence of a nation over its coastal waters, the territorial ambitions of most coastal nations stretched only to the limit of territorial waters. This was the three mile limit. A few more powerful nations took upon themselves the exercise of power in waters outside the territorial waters of smaller nations. In the mid-twentieth century this situation changed as greater use of the sea and its resources made three miles seem an absurdly small distance from the coast. Twelve miles became a more common limit, internationally accepted and promulgated by one nation after another.

NEW SPHERES OF INFLUENCE

The desire both to profit from oil resources much further off the coast and to control foreign over-fishing, where depleted fish stocks were hazarding the livelihood of local fishermen, led to spheres of influence for many countries, but not territorial waters, being pushed much further off shore. These went to two hundred miles or more. This led to outer limits overlapping those of other countries. Where this occurred in north west Europe, median lines were established, leading to an irregular pattern of areas on the chart. For the United Kingdom, whose area is squashed in by Continental European countries on one side and Eire on the other, the limits make a long, thin, area oriented in a north–south direction. This stretches towards the Arctic Circle in the north, where a narrow strip reaches to 200 miles north of the northern tip of the Shetland Isles, and towards Spain in the south, where a 'trouser leg' shape stretches to 200 miles in a southerly direction from the Scilly Isles. In the middle, one side is limited by the median line in the English Channel and North Sea, the other by those in the Irish Sea and north west Approaches.

The pattern of irregular areas formed by boundaries and median lines, often sub-divided by individual nations, has come to be known as the 'Offshore Tapestry'. Within the bounds of a nation's offshore tapestry is the area where it exercises its economic influence. Within it lie its oil and gas rigs, its control of fishing and its sea-bed mining. Whilst foreign warships do not have a right to enter a nation's territorial waters, all vessels have the right to operate in the remainder of a nation's offshore tapestry, except in small areas established for safety reasons around oil and gas rigs.

There remain many areas off the coasts of the world where overlapping boundaries have not been resolved by mutually agreed median lines. The sea areas lying

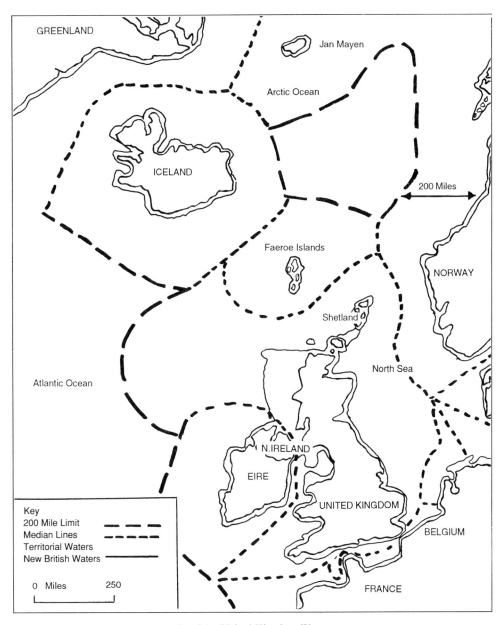

Fig. 3.1   United Kingdom Waters

between these overlapping boundaries provide causes for tension at low levels, or even conflict. The accuracy of modern navigation systems is, however, preventing offshore patrol vessels from inadvertently entering these disputed areas, thus reducing the opportunities for conflict where it is not intended. Where offshore patrol vessels find it necessary to enter these areas, the swift and reliable voice communications systems now installed in these ships allow their shore headquarters to be well briefed and their own nation to keep the other nation informed, so avoiding any possible misunderstanding that could arise.

Policeman on the beat

There is much wealth in the offshore tapestry, particularly when a continental shelf runs well out towards the outer boundary. Where there is wealth there is crime. In peace the offshore patrol vessel acts as the eyes and information gatherer in its patrol area. To the local fisherman who is abiding by his quota, the vessel is a friendly confidence booster. To the foreign fishing vessel without rights to fish in the area, the OPV is a deterrent. To the oil rig placed well offshore and exposed to terrorist action, the OPV is again seen as a deterrent, whilst it is seen as a law enforcer when a fishing vessel enters the rig's exclusion area. The OPV is therefore a policeman on the beat in its area. In the UK offshore tapestry areas, the Commanding Officer has the right to enforce fishing vessels suspected of infringement of fishing regulations to proceed into port for further investigation. However, whilst an OPV could restore order on an oil or gas rig, since it stands on the sea bed, a rig is, in effect, a mini island and hence needs the shore-side police force to carry out arrests.

There are other ways in which the OPV plays the policeman's role. By being in the area the unusual is noticed, the drug runner or illegal immigrant chain uncovered, the foreign warship anchored in the area reported, the drifting fishing vessel with a line around its screw helped, assistance given in putting out a fire onboard a ferry and tackling an oil slick with dispersant carried onboard. In effect, the OPV upholds the friendly and confident tradition of the local 'bobby' on the beat.

Who pays for the policeman? For countries that have a dedicated coastguard organisation tasked with offshore patrol (such as the United States), the funding of the policemen on the beat is a simple Government apportionment to the Ministry controlling the coastguard. For those where there is no separate coastguard organisation, or where, as in Britain, it is not given the offshore patrol task, funding becomes considerably more involved.

Offshore patrol is not a glamorous naval task and hence does not command a reasonable slice of the naval budget. Navies faced with an offshore patrol task welcome the chance for young Commanding Officers to gain experience in relatively independent commands. They also welcome the presence of naval vessels around the coast and the publicity that occurs when they are involved in rescue or other events that make the newspaper headlines. But they do not welcome expenditure of scarce naval funds on tasks that are not seen as directly relating to their naval responsibilities. On the assumption that to achieve their prime task the best method of defence against the maritime enemy is to fight the battle on the 'blue waters', well away from one's own coast, larger navies tend to consider coastal warfare as a very secondary call on their budget. One exception is where coastal warfare directly impacts on the ability of the blue water element to undertake their task (eg: the need to keep the approaches to the Clyde clear of mines to allow free passage of the SSBNs).

A recent statement by the Royal Navy's then First Sea Lord that the offshore task was an important element of the Royal Navy's commitment has led some to speculate on whether this was generated by the much reduced menace of the Soviet maritime threat, or by the dwindling size of the Royal Navy, causing a small navy outlook. In either event, the statement was welcome to those who are convinced of the importance of a naval presence permanently carrying out the various tasks around the UK coast.

Large navies look for other sources of funding for the tasks for which they consider they should not be paying. Hence, in the United Kingdom, other ministries such as the Ministry of Agriculture, Fisheries and Food (for fishery protection) and the Department of Energy (for oil and gas rig protection) contribute to the cost of building and running the Royal Navy's OPVs. Somewhat differently, the Department of Agriculture and Fishery in Scotland takes responsibility for the fishery protection patrol of the offshore tapestry area to the north-west of Scotland, providing its own unarmed civilian manned OPVs and the necessary shore control. This leads to duplication of vessels in the areas when other offshore patrol tasks require the presence of the Royal Navy.

The fashion for the strict accounting economies of privatisation has caused the English Ministry of Agriculture, Fisheries and Food to question the costs of the Royal Navy offshore patrol force and examine whether the service would not be more cheaply provided by contracting it out to a civilian firm. This option was chosen in the Falkland Islands when licences and fishery control were established in the offshore waters around the islands. But the civilian vessels are unarmed and it is considered wise that a Royal Naval OPV of the *Castle* class should be in these waters to provide a back up and undertake the other offshore tasks.

In the United Kingdom, those pressing the need and the advantages to the Royal Navy of having naval OPVs as the sole patrol effort in the UK offshore tapestry, found themselves facing two sets of opponents, the 'privatisers' and those in the Naval Staff who thought that scarce money would be better spent on blue water warships. UK fishermen lobbied their MPs on the need to retain the Royal Navy in the task, pointing out that it was unacceptable to them that their policeman on the beat should be a civilian firm contracted to undertake the job. On that occasion the Royal Navy retained its tasks but the Royal Air Force task of air patrol of the offshore tapestry was taken over, either by civilian aircraft owned by the civilian Ministries or chartered by them. The argument for privatising the fishery protection task overlooks the purely naval tasks that would still remain with the Royal Navy. It is a subject that will remain topical whilst commercial firms continue to see the opportunity to make a profit from taking on the job.

Co-ordinated air and sea patrols An OPV cannot cover all of its area all the time. The aim is therefore to be in the right place at the right time. To achieve this, some assistance in the air is needed to cover the whole patrol area. This will allow an assessment to be made of the most profitable section of its area in which an OPV should patrol. The best solution for an OPV is an embarked helicopter. However, noting the size of an average OPV, the requirements of flight deck, hangar, helicopter maintenance and operating personnel make an organic helicopter an unlikely feature in the design. It has been achieved in larger Norwegian and

Danish OPVs and, with oil rig protection in mind, the Royal Navy's Castle class has a flight deck and long range air radar, but no hangar, allowing the ship temporarily to carry a helicopter of reasonable size. Although ingenious folding hangars have been used in ships, such additions go against the tenet that OPVs should be the cheapest ships that can undertake the task. Air patrol must normally, therefore, come from shore based aircraft.

It is natural that a country first looks to its naval air arm or airforce to provide patrols to support OPVs in the offshore areas. It is desirable that the aircraft chosen for the task be fitted with a radar that can detect large numbers of smaller vessels and craft and present the contacts in a digestible manner. This leads to the choice of a Maritime Patrol Aircraft (MPA). Because of their prime task, these aircraft have sophisticated equipment and are designed to stay for long periods on patrol in the blue water areas. Although expensive to operate in the offshore tapestry, such aircraft as the *Nimrod* and the *Orion* are more than adequately equipped to support the OPV. There are smaller Maritime Patrol Aircraft (MPA) designed specifically for the offshore waters, but these have yet to find many customers. Indeed, when the UK privatised offshore air patrol, it did not turn to the modern small MPA, but to simpler and cheaper aircraft such as the *Islander* and *Dornier*, or in Scotland where the conditions are worse and distances greater, an older *Fokker F28* fitted with radar.

For aircraft and OPV to co-operate successfully, good and secure communications are necessary as well as a simple method of passing positions accurately. For the period whilst the aircraft is operating in the OPV's area, it must be effectively employed to produce the best intelligence for the OPV, as well as the vessel distribution details required to build up the statistics held ashore. These are needed to produce reliable predictions for the future. Whilst it sounds simple, for the aircraft to effectively carry out its task with the minimum of radio transmissions, on specific frequencies, good basic drills and practice are required by both the aircraft and OPV. Combined with this is the need for regular liaison between crews when ashore. This establishes the personal contact that is necessary for good co-operation, particularly when dealing with a combination of civilian and military units.

An aircraft on patrol can only photograph and report what is happening on the sea. Photographs can be useful evidence if the culprit subsequently enters one of your own harbours and can be arrested, but they do not replace the detailed evidence of geographical position and offence that an OPV can generate, combined with its ability physically to require the offender to proceed to a nominated port. To undertake these tasks requires good position fixing equipment in OPVs, together with a reliable system of recording position and movement which is accepted as evidence in Court, and cameras for clearly recording the details of the offence. The OPV's gun provides a forceful incentive for the offender to comply. This is something that the aircraft cannot do with the precision necessary to avoid undue damage or bloodshed.

Immigration Control

Prevention of those attempting to become illegal immigrants is not a normal naval task, but navies have frequently been drawn into this employment for lack

PLATE 3.1 HMDS *Vaedderen* is one of five frigate-type OPVs operated by the Royal Danish Navy around the Faeroes and off the coast of Greenland. She operates a *Lynx Mk 80/91* helicopter and has a *Siemens-Plessey AWS-6* surveillance radar. (*Photo: HM Steele*)

PLATE 3.2   A Breguet *Atlantique* maritime patrol aircraft, in the service of the German Navy. (*Photo: German Navy*)

PLATE 3.3   The Dornier *DO 28* general purpose maritime patrol aircraft. (*Photo: German Navy*)

of anyone else to undertake it at sea. Whilst, as we have seen, frigates have been used for immigration control in the past, eg: Royal Naval frigates off the Palestinian coast in the late forties and off the southern Bahamas in the sixties, OPVs are the more usual choice. Predominant in this task have been the Royal Navy's *Peacock* class in Hong Kong waters. With their good speed and relatively low freeboard, a contrast to the average OPV which is designed with heavy weather in mind, these OPVs have been very successful at intercepting the flow of illegal immigrants into Hong Kong.

For the task of intercepting illegal immigrants the OPV needs to look like a warship in order to act as a deterrent. It also needs a fast boat to catch those who are outpacing the OPV, scrambling nets for the ship's sides, additional food and space to accommodate the immigrants whilst onboard. As illegal immigrants are often in unseaworthy boats, the OPV employed on this task must be able to operate in heavy weather well off shore in order to rescue those illegal immigrants in difficulties. The author has experience of embarking 200 intended illegal immigrants on one occasion and also of rescuing some in heavy seas from a raft on which they had set out to drift to their destination.

Anti-terrorist patrols and oil rig protection Standing alone 180 miles offshore pumping 'liquid gold' that is an essential energy source for the nation, the oil or gas rig is a very tempting target for the terrorist seeking maximum disruption and publicity. For this reason, governments have given considerable attention to their plans for the protection of these rigs. The OPV is the most regular representative of the Government to visit these remote monsters standing high out of the sea. In any sea state the rigs are difficult to board from the water, but not beyond the competence of determined terrorists trained as divers. Arrival by helicopter is a more simple method which can be achieved in most weathers. An OPV with a primary task of rig protection therefore profits if it has a helicopter embarked.

Because it is already on patrol, it is likely that an OPV will be the first warship on the scene after an incident has occurred and will become the Scene of Operations Commander. To undertake this task the OPV must have comprehensive, reliable and instant communications so that it can talk with the rig, its own boat or helicopter, its personnel placed on the rig, the Command Headquarters ashore, the Police Force Headquarters in whose area the rig stands, other warships that have been called in to assist and any special forces that are brought from shore to raid the rig. If the rig has been held hostage by a determined group of terrorists, a wide range of military capability will be needed if the rig is to be retaken without undue loss of life or damage. Since it is not economic to retain defence forces on all the many rigs, it must be demonstrated that a rig can be recovered without terrorists achieving any form of success. The OPV on patrol is the visible presence that indicates that this capability exists. We have already noted that as a rig is technically land, the shore police must be swiftly brought to a rig after an incident. Once the rig is recovered by military forces, it is only the police who can charge and arrest suspects.

Patrols against terrorists landing on the coast or gun running to shore have been a long standing task. Off Northern Ireland the Royal Navy employ patrol vessels of the *Bird* and *Ton* classes to operate in the lochs and coastal waters. Whilst they perform a good deterrent role, unless they have some previous intelligence information, their chances of coming upon a terrorist or gun runner in the course of their patrols and boarding are not high. To achieve this task, the vessels need a reasonable turn of speed, a good surface radar, a fast boat and a trained and armed boarding party.

Drug surveillance, anti-smuggling and anti-pirate patrols The term pirate has dropped from use in modern times when life is so structured and organised that such persons are no longer considered to exist. The Royal Navy's Ton class conducted anti-pirate patrols in the Gulf and off Borneo for many years. Whilst the development of nations in these areas has reduced the incidence of piracy, the publicity given to Vietnamese boat people, who suffered at the hands of pirates, has reminded everyone that they do still exist. Indeed, large western merchant vessels transiting the Malacca Straits now carry pistols close at hand to deal with pirates who have well organised methods of scaling an underway merchant ship's side by night. Once onboard they act in the same manner as any thief or burglar before leaving the ship as quietly as they arrived.

Suppression of piracy has traditionally been an offshore task and remains so. Whilst there are still traditional pirates in certain waters around the world, the modern equivalent of the original pirate is the arms smuggler or drug runner. An OPV is unlikely to detect vessels used for these purposes in the course of its normal patrol duties unless it has previous intelligence, or comes upon vessels transferring items between them away from normal anchorages. This is always a suspicious act as even oil has been fraudulently transferred between tankers. Given good intelligence, an OPV on patrol can intercept, shadow and report a suspected vessel until it enters territorial waters and can be searched. To carry out this type of work an OPV needs a reasonable speed, a gun to act as a deterrent and good navigation and recording facilities.

FISHERY PROTECTION

Fishery Protection is probably the oldest of the offshore patrol tasks. It started with the aim of protecting local boats from foreigners wanting to fish where good quality fish could easily be caught. The task steadily increased and in the 1890s the Royal Navy formed a permanent Fishery Protection Squadron. By then Hull and Fleetwood trawlers were fishing in distant waters off Greenland, Iceland, North Norway and the White Sea. The Royal Navy's task was more to provide assistance to small trawlers at great distance from their home port than to provide protection. Assistance was mostly in the form of breakdown repair and medical aid. At that stage the only conservation aspect of the patrol was to ensure that net sizes and the size of fish onboard conformed to international standards. Through to the sixties these Hull and Fleetwood trawlers fished in large numbers along the 100 fathom lines in those northern waters. They faced heavy weather, intense cold and the winter danger of icing up, but the profits were good and the difficulties and dangers worth it. They created little outposts of northern England on these remote patches of water. Trawlers broke off from the group when their holds were full and set off for their home port, whilst empty vessels arrived to take their place in the never changing line of trawlers.

As the Royal Navy then had no OPVs, *Algerine* class minesweepers performed the distant waters fishery protection task, to be relieved in the latter half of the fifties by small frigates of the *Type 14* class. These warships were not designed for distant water work, having a low upper deck and exposed superstructure. However it was soon found that if the high bows were put head to sea these 1500-ton frigates could survive in the worst winter conditions. Their lightly constructed hulls soon suffered cracks and the class were all strengthened on the ship's side amidships, to allow them to continue this task. Their worst problem was that they were single screw ships with only one of each piece of machinery. This created the need for an inventive engineering department who knew that if anything broke, getting the ship home depended on fixing the problem onboard. Although the *Type 14s* gave good service in these distant waters, they were an object lesson in how an independently operating offshore patrol vessel should *not* be designed.

Whilst the *Algerines* and the *Type 14s* operated in the distant waters, the *Ton* class carried out the fishery protection task around the United Kingdom. At that stage, legal control of fishing extended only out to the limit of territorial waters. An exception to this was the North Sea where the countries bordering the area agreed that their fishery protection vessels could operate throughout it, carrying out the net measuring and checking task. Intensive fishing of the North Sea, primarily by groups of Soviet trawlers, led to much reduced stocks and a desire for more extensive conservation measures. When areas were closed to certain types of fishing, enforcement provided a new task for the OPV.

The desire to control the seas to a greater distance from the coast occurred around the time of Britain's entry to the European Community. Community law on fishing has developed fast and because the regulations are amended so frequently, the 'policeman on the beat' has to have the books close to hand on the Bridge. In the OPV's offshore tapestry area there may be many different sections where the catching of certain species are banned at different times of year, where certain non-Community vessels are allowed to fish because of historic rights, where maximum net sizes vary, or where the maximum take of any one species in one vessel must not be more than a certain percentage. Fishery protection has therefore become very much a law enforcement task for the OPV.

Other nations have, of course, also enacted similar regulations, thus forcing the distant water trawlers to withdraw and so ending the distant waters patrols. However, an OPV operating in the offshore tapestry some 200 miles north of Shetland is as exposed as any distant water vessel was.

One small aspect of fishery protection that provides variety for the fishery protection vessels is the cat and mouse task of catching salmon poachers using nets off estuaries. This work needs good intelligence, a fast boat or helicopter and a good nerve.

OPVs engaged in fishery protection require particular equipment if they are to be effective. Needed are:

▶ At least two good inflatable boats with a good speed;

▶ A gun to act as a deterrent;

▶ An accurate and reliable navigation system which displays the tracks of other vessels and automatically recorded;

▶ A good surface radar with an air capability or a separate air radar to control helicopters and establish positions of co-operating aircraft;

▶ Good communications compatible with those in modern fishing vessels;

▶ A radio receiver that searches VHF radio channels and locks to whichever one is transmitting;

▶ A good medical outfit;

▶ Diving equipment that will allow divers to clear ropes from fishing vessels' propellers;

▶ A hull that can stand up to heavy weather and, if the vessel is large enough, have the capability to carry a helicopter.

PLATE 3.4   The German Ministry of Agriculture and Fisheries operates six OPVs converted from commercial craft. The *Meerkatze* displaces 2250 tons and has a top speed of 15 knots. (*Photo: Fr Lurssenwerft*)

PLATE 3.5   NCGV *Senja*, one of the *Nordkapp* class in its icebreaker role, shows that in some parts of the world, free navigation depends on the activities of coastal forces.(*Photo: Royal Norwegian Navy*)

Embarked in the OPV must be an officer qualified in the appropriate fishing law and regulations, equipped with net gauges, copies of National and European Community regulations and a system ashore that promptly provides him with changes to the regulations and intelligence of fishing vessel movements. The Commanding Officer must have qualified as a Sea Fisheries Officer with the power to detain fishing vessels and take them into harbour.

OTHER TASKS

Oil Dispersant

A small but, on occasions, essential task of an OPV on patrol is to disperse oil slicks that it encounters. To do this the vessel requires internal tanks for dispersant fluid, a pumping capacity and spray booms that can be swung out from the hull on either side of the ship. As with many other OPV tasks, a capability to control or co-ordinate the many other units from various sources that may be taking part is essential.

Yacht Race and Other Escort Duties

The OPV is a good choice when a naval authority is committed to provide an escort at sea for some function. Most usually this is an offshore yacht race. Whilst it sounds a simple task, in addition to being able to operate in bad weather it has other requirements. Good radio equipment compatible with yacht radios is essential, together with good communications ashore, both to report the progress of the yachts and for the embarked press to send their articles. Also needed is a good radar coverage and a comprehensive plotting facility, medical equipment and knowledge, the ability to carry out minor repairs to yachts in distress and scrambling nets for the ship's side to embark survivors in heavy weather, together with spare accommodation and food. If a helicopter can be carried this will greatly reduce the amount of sea that the OPV must cover to check on those of its charges that do not respond to radio calls. Whilst no navy would add to the expense of an OPV design purely to provide assistance to yachts, these requirements take their place in the assessment of what should be in an OPV design.

Showing the Flag and Recruiting

Any warship represents its nation, regardless of size. The image that it portrays is one of the nation it represents. An OPV design will be primarily based on the requirements of the task that it must perform, but the naval architect will attempt to give the vessel a smart and efficient appearance. It then falls to the crew to keep their ship in a condition that impresses those who see it. In theory the warship is 'showing the Flag' whenever it is away from its base where it is probably out of sight of all but those directly concerned with the vessel.

On some occasions an OPV can be programmed for a 'Flag showing' visit to a smaller port for a specific celebration, or to encourage a career in the Navy amongst the youth of the port area. Such visits require the OPV to be in a smart and clean condition. It will probably call for the officers and ship's company to entertain dignitaries or groups of people from ashore, so the vessel will need a Commanding Officer's cabin or a Wardroom suitable for this task. A space on the upper deck where an awning can be spread in warmer weather is desirable, as is the ability to 'dress ship' with flags from stem to stern. Floodlighting the ship after sunset is helpful to the aim of the visit and equipment needs to be carried for this. If the OPV is fitted with a gun or missile system or carries a helicopter, it adds to the success of the visit, particularly where recruiting is concerned.

Exercises for War

An OPV, unlike most other warships, has a major task in peacetime. All warships have their task in war and the OPV is not exempt from this. Whilst other classes of warship are occupied on training for war or carrying out some form of operational task, the OPV is going about its business. Numbers of OPVs in a navy therefore need to be larger than the number required for the peacetime offshore task, so that OPVs have time to train for their war tasks. Because of the demands on the time of an OPV in peacetime, war training needs to be a well structured and testing period, intense and productive. As OPVs operate independently in peacetime there is only a limited amount of war training that they can do whilst on patrol. Training periods must therefore cover all that training for the war task that cannot be done independently. It needs to be done in company with other ships to provide the spur of competition and a method for the crew to assess their own performance against that of others. An experienced 'work up' staff is needed to plan, implement and comment on the performance of the training. This training should include both the ability of the OPV to survive in war and for it to accomplish the tasks that it will be expected to carry out.

For an OPV to be efficient at its peacetime tasks, its crew must be confident that they can perform effectively in war. Hence an OPV will provide the same standard in performing its peace tasks that its nation would expect from a warship in war.

4

Offshore Patrol in a Period of Tension

An OPV's peacetime tasks will continue into the beginning of a period of tension that could lead to war. The task of the policeman on the beat becomes even more important at this time.

Surveilliance

As tension increases, the urgency of some of the new tasks that will arise overtakes the peacetime tasks. The first of these new tasks, for which OPVs are likely to be needed, is that of surveillance of potentially hostile vessels in the offshore tapestry. Such vessels may be apparently innocent fishing vessels that have the capability to lay mines off the entrances to important ports, report the movement of warships or intercept radio communications. They may be vessels attempting to land parties ashore illegally, or may even be minor or major warships operating in the offshore tapestry, either with the aim of bringing pressure to bear or positioning themselves for hostilities. Whatever their aim, it is necessary to know where they are and to keep them under observation.

Whilst aircraft may be able to revisit an area frequently and, subject to the weather, report positions of suspicious or potentially hostile vessels, it is the surface vessel that will demonstrate the will to control events in its own offshore tapestry area. Part of this demonstration is to show that the movements of potentially hostile vessels will be closely followed and all activity recorded. Such close surveillance may also prevent the covert minelayer from attempting to lay his mines for fear of displaying the intentions of his country. The most economical method of achieving this task is with an OPV. Such use also allows more major warships to continue their preparations for war.

Thorough surveillance of a suspicious vessel requires the ability to remain at sea in all weathers, to have a long range—so that the OPV can stay with the target, to have enough speed to keep the target within range and to have the photographic capability to record any suspicious activity. A range of desirable requirements, such as good EW equipment to monitor the target's transmissions, could only be found in major warships, which at this time would probably be in harbour storing for war, or working up their weapon systems and training to a peak.

PLATE 4.1   To replace the older OPVs the Royal Danish Navy has ordered four *IS-86* type inspection ships of the *Thetis* class. These 100m ships are capable of being up-graded in time of emergency. (*Photo: Royal Danish Navy Material Command*)

Marking

As tension increases towards a higher risk of war, potential enemy warships may position themselves for a co-ordinated first strike. This may involve the deployment of ships with long range missiles, operating singly at near their maximum range from their targets, whether these are ships at sea, a naval base or some other land target. The OPV may have previously been carrying out surveillance on the suspect ship. Once it is realised that the possible enemy is positioning himself for a co-ordinated strike, surveillance changes to marking. The aim of marking is to ensure that if an enemy vessel fires at a target, he is certainly going to sustain damage from the marker. The marker can also alert the world.

The marker must aim to demonstrate his intentions by staying reasonably close to the potential enemy warship, if necessary keeping his gun trained at it. As the enemy vessel will also wish to destroy the marker, the latter must be ready to open fire instantly the moment the enemy makes his first hostile move. By now the reader will have appreciated that marking a potential enemy warship is really no job for an OPV that will almost certainly be at a serious disadvantage the moment hostilities begin. However, it is a task that the OPV could well find itself undertaking until relieved by one of its own major warships.

Route Survey

In peacetime, as we shall see in more detail in Chapter 12, minehunters establish the details of the sea bed along routes to be used in war. This involves detailed work to record and chart every object so that in war the presence of new objects can be quickly established, investigated and classified as mines or otherwise.

In a period of tension it is necessary to check routes regularly to ensure that mines have not been laid. This can be achieved by a vessel towing a side scan sonar, the picture received being checked against the previously recorded details.

PLATE 4.2 The new French '*frégates de surveillance*' of the *Floréal* class are a
belated attempt to make good the shortage of escorts. They are armed with a
100 mm gun forward and have a helicopter hangar and flight deck aft (*Photo: GEC
-Alsthom/Ch. de L'Atlantique*)

If the correlation of the chart against the new details is to be possible, good position fixing systems are necessary. To ensure the safety of the vessel against activation of newly laid mines whilst it is towing the sonar, it should preferably be a
vessel with a low magnetic signature and hence be a minehunter. However, available minehunters will be fully occupied on more important minewarfare tasks at
this time. The OPV is therefore a likely candidate for the task of fast route survey
in a period of tension. As the side scan sonar is towed astern, a good degaussing
system in the OPV, to help reduce its magnetic signature, will also reduce the risk.
Whilst this is a less risky task for the OPV than marking, it is one that will not
encourage much relaxation amongst the crew.

Coastal Convoy Administrative Escort

As tension increases further, it may be decided that coastal convoys should be
run in the offshore waters. This procedure is adopted more to establish control
over movements of merchant ships than for their protection. With merchant ships

gathered together into a coastal convoy they can be routed through safer areas of water, easily diverted from areas of danger and readily identified. Even without an escort of warships, the presence of a large group provides some form of mutual protection should they come across an unknown minefield, be attacked by aircraft or meet up with an aggressive potential enemy warship.

Without a major warship escort, a coastal convoy lacks central control and communications. This is the task that falls to the OPV. An embarked Coastal Convoy Commodore can provide the command of the convoy. The good communications outfit of an OPV can provide the links both with the civil communication systems of the merchant ships and the naval communications system to the shore headquarters, thus reducing the amount of traffic that must be passed ashore at a time when communications to naval headquarters will be at a maximum. The OPV, with its good navigation system, can ensure that the convoy navigates precisely along the centre of the nominated routes and hence reduce the width of the routes that have previously had to be searched. The OPV can therefore usefully accomplish the task of Coastal Convoy Administrative Escort.

Landing Parties on Potentially Hostile Coastlines

Most OPVs do not have the speed or low profile that is necessary for covert work off potentially hostile coasts. But some, such as the *Peacock* class used in Hong Kong waters by the Royal Navy and off the Irish coast by the Irish Navy, have an ability to undertake this task. Good, fast, inflatable boats, with a swift method of lowering and hoisting them, are an essential for this task. However, it is one that will rarely fall to the average OPV.

PLATE 4.3 The LCM *A1432* displaces 60 tons and can carry 50 men, and is of the type that could be used for landing small parties on hostile shores.
(Photo: German Navy)

PLATE 4.4   South Korea's Coastguard operates two *Bukhansan* type 50m OPVs.
No 278 is armed with a twin 40mm 1/70 Breda gun mounting forward, controlled
by a Radamec electro-optical director (*Photo: Radamec*)

Pickets

The picket warship operating alone in its nominated position using its 'eyes and ears' is a very traditional naval task. Nelson used his smaller warships as pickets to provide him with intelligence of the enemy's movements. In more modern times, the naval picket has been more associated with an air defence ship placed to give early warning of air attack. An OPV fitted with air warning radar can undertake a basic version of this task and the Royal Navy has used the *Castle* class in Falkland waters to act as air pickets. Depending on the equipment fitted, all OPVs could be an option for this task.

5
Offshore Patrol in War

Some of the OPV's peacetime tasks will extend into war, particularly that of fishery protection. Whilst it is important that the nation is fed and therefore that the nation's fishing vessels should be shepherded in safe fishing areas, the fishery protection task is likely to receive a lower priority in the face of the many other tasks for which the OPV will be wanted. At this stage it will be possible to take up from trade vessels that could perform the OPV role where this requires little or no armament. These are likely to be deep sea trawlers, larger rig support vessels, where they can be spared, and millionaires' large yachts. The genuine offshore patrol vessel is normally lightly armed and not designed for war. But in war there is always a shortage of warships and the OPV will inevitably be pressed into service in areas for which it was not specifically designed. The task of Coastal Convoy Administrative Escort, which has already been described, will continue to require many OPVs if the convoy system has been instituted. There are also other important tasks for which OPVs will be required.

PLATE 5.1   The German Coastal Minehunter *Lindau*. (*Photo: German Navy*)

Minehunter and Minesweeper Support

There are never enough minewarfare forces to go round when mining is a threat. To minimise this shortage, it is essential to keep the hunters and sweepers on task for the maximum time possible. Long passages to their base for fuel, water, food, or ready use spares and stores can be avoided if a support vessel is close at hand to provide them. With their relatively large fuel capacity and ample storage space, the OPV is a likely choice for this task. If it has a flight deck which will allow a helicopter to deliver urgently required spares and stores, this will avoid the support vessel being off task to collect them at a time when its resources may urgently be required to keep an MCM vessel on task.

Since mine countermeasures operations will often be in one's own coastal areas, the light arming of the OPV is not a serious disadvantage. However, where there is a threat additional to that of the mine, the support vessel must be held further back and a major warship made available to provide cover for the MCM forces on task. The Royal Navy have found this procedure necessary in some of their recent MCM operations in the Gulf.

Minefield Gate Patrol

Traditional style minefields off ports have a fixed channel with a 'gate' at the seaward end. To monitor who enters the channel, a gate patrol can be maintained. Modern minefields are more sophisticated, with moving channels and entrances. This sophistication makes it even more necessary that there should be a gate patrol to ensure that one's own vessels enter at the right place. In minefields that

PLATE 5.2   Coastal mine warfare ships can be kept on station much longer with the
help of Mine Depot Ships like the German *Mosel*. (*Photo: German Navy*)

extend well to seaward in the offshore tapestry, this is a task that must be done in all weathers. The average, robust OPV can cope well with this boring, but essential, task.

Despatch Vessel

Navies through the ages have had purpose built Despatch Vessels which were small greyhounds of the Fleet. The last Despatch Vessels in the Royal Navy were converted from frigates to operate under this title, but hardly fitted the traditional description. They were paid off in the 1950s and it was assumed that the historical title had died. However, in the Falklands war task force it was found that Despatch vessels were necessary and OPVs of the *Castle* class operated in the front line under this title. Being lightly armed and without the damage control capability of a major warship, their crews must have felt exposed whilst they went about their tasks in the middle of the landing phase.

Warfare in Shallow Waters

Some warships built for offshore patrol have been employed more on warfare tasks in the offshore tapestry than on patrols. Being smaller than the average major warship, they are well suited for warfare in more shallow waters. The Royal Navy has built such vessels. Examples are the heavy gunned, shallow draft vessels, such as HMS *Erebus*, that were in service up to the Second World War and the small anti-submarine frigates of the *Type 14* class in service from the fifties to the seventies. Except for one Indian Navy *Type 14* sunk in the war with Pakistan, the vessels of this class spent their entire life on offshore patrol duties or on exercises.

Warfare can occur in the shallower waters of the offshore tapestry, such as the English Channel, and this is acknowledged by the increasing sophistication in the design of OPVs. The demand for OPVs with a good warfare capability is therefore strong. However, there is a choice for this specific task between a well armed, large OPV, or a more expensive small frigate, such as the 1100 ton General Purpose 'mini frigate' designed by Swan Hunter.

6
Offshore Patrol Vessels

Many vessels are used in the offshore patrol role, but this chapter concentrates on vessels specifically *designed* or converted for work in the offshore tapestry.

Inshore Patrol Vessels

There were formerly many types of vessel in the larger navies designed for work in the inner areas of the offshore tapestry. In the Royal Navy there were large numbers of the *Ham* and *Ford* classes, designed for other purposes but converted over the years for use as patrol craft, training craft, inshore survey craft and even as degaussing vessels.

A specific design for patrol work was the Royal Netherlands Navy *Balder* class. The dimensions of these vessels were:

Overall length	119 feet (36.3 metres)
Beam	20 feet (6.2 metres)
Average Draft	6 ft 4 ins (1.9 metres)
Displacement	169 tons
Engine	300 hp
Maximum speed	15.5 knots
Armament	1 40mm gun
	3 20mm guns
	Depth charges
Complement	26 men

The large size of the crew, in comparison with the size of the vessel, looks a little out of place in these days of economy of manpower. However these vessels did sterling work off the Dutch coast for many years, but their low freeboard limited their activity in bad weather.

A more modern class of smaller patrol craft is the Royal Navy's *Bird* class. Derived from a Royal Air Force design of air-sea rescue craft, the *Bird* class have needed extensive modification and they are not the best vessels in poor weather. They are usefully employed as training craft for the Royal Naval College at Dartmouth and for patrol of northern Irish waters. The 30 knot Brooke Marine design of the *Fremantle* class patrol vessel for the Royal Australian Navy was a more successful product of around the same period.

A more recent design is the 33m design of Vosper Thornycroft, which has been adopted by the US Coastguard and built by the Louisiana based Bollinger yard.

PLATE 6.1   The Netherlands Navy Balder class HMN1S *Hadda* (*Photo: Royal Netherlands Navy*)

Judging by the large numbers being built in the United States, this must be a successful vessel. A later design is the recently built *Abdullah* class for the Jordanian Navy.

Moving up one size, the Royal Navy's *Ton* class have been used for patrolling in many parts of the world, stretching from the north of Scotland to Gibraltar, Cyprus, the Gulf, the Malacca Straits, the waters off northern Borneo and Hong Kong. Large numbers of this class of wooden hulled vessels were built as minesweepers in the fifties. Many were converted to minehunters and some to patrol craft, but all were used at some stage in the role of patrol craft. One of this class, HMS *Wilton* was built with a glass reinforced fibre (GRP) hull. It was the first vessel in the world to use this material for a warship of this size. *Ton* class vessels have been sold to many other navies and have patrolled in waters around the world. Now 30–35 years old, some of them continue to give good service.

Purpose Built OPVs

To replace the *Ton* class patrol vessels operating in the Far East, the Royal Navy introduced the *Peacock* class built by Hall Russell. These vessels were partly paid for by the Hong Kong Government and were specifically designed for the tasks in the Hong Kong coastal waters and offshore tapestry. They are fast vessels with a capable gun. Their relatively low freeboard allows the easy despatch of their inflatable boat and its recovery with illegal immigrants. Two of this class also serve in the Irish Navy. Other versions of this design, with improved fire control equipment and surface-to-surface missiles, have been built for Middle Eastern navies.

The core design of current offshore patrol vessels is probably that of the Royal Navy's *Island* class. This design was the first to move away from the

PLATE 6.2   HMAS *Launceston, a Fremantle* class patrol boat. (*Photo: Royal Australian Navy*)

naval designed hull and adopt a commercial design solution. These vessels were based on the traditional robust trawler hull, renowned for its ability to ride out any storm. Designed and built by the Hall Russell shipyard at Aberdeen, the *Island* class have proved reliable and capable within the limitations of their design. The vessels are strong, but lack normal naval standards of shock resistance, fire-fighting capability and damage control. Designed originally to take an Oto Melara gun, which was also fitted to the *Peacock* class, the *Island* class were eventually provided with an older 40mm Bofors gun, which left them lightly armed. These guns came from ex-Second World War stock and were over 20 years old when fitted. However, they have served their purpose.

Life can be hard in rough weather in an *Island* class 200 miles north of the Shetlands. To compensate for this, as there is less pressure on space in a lightly armed warship than in a large and more sophisticated vessel, accommodation has been provided to civilian crew standards with six berth cabins for

PLATE 6.3   Jordanian *Abdullah* Patrol Craft (*Photo: Vosper Thorneycroft*)

the junior crew members, recreation rooms and a large galley. Details of the Island class are:

Length	195 feet (59.6m)
Beam	36 feet (11m)
Draft	14 feet (4.3m)
Displacement	1260 tons full load
Engines	2 Diesels giving 4380hp
Maximum Speed	16.5 knots
Armament	1 × 40mm gun
Equipment	2 × fast inflatable craft
	Oil dispersant storage and booms
	VHF communication monitoring
Crew	39 men

Both the Government Departments concerned with fisheries and with energy supplied by offshore oil rigs contribute towards the cost of the *Island* class, a useful contribution to the Naval budget.

PLATE 6.4 The Royal Navy GRP *Ton* class HMS *Wilton* (*Photo: Vosper Thorneycroft*)

PLATE 6.5 HMS *Alderney*, one of the Royal Navy's *Island* class of patrol vessels. Note the North Sea oil rig in the background (*Photo: S Haines*)

After the *Island* class, the next development for the Royal Navy was the *Castle* class. Also designed and built by Hall Russell at Aberdeen, these vessels are longer than the *Islands* (266 feet–81m) and more comfortable in heavy weather. This extra length provides a flight deck, and the improved stability allows the ship to operate all the classes of helicopter at present at sea with the Royal Navy. Two of this class went south with the Falklands Task Force to operate as Despatch Vessels and one still serves in the South Atlantic on OPV duties. During the war in the Falklands, one of the *Castles* proved that, in emergency, it was possible to operate helicopters of the size of the *Chinook* from its flight deck.

Only two *Castle* class OPVs were built. The ships are very capable for their role and this, unfortunately, led to the premature abandonment of the class. Seeing their capability, it was decided to upgrade the class and a design requirement known as OPV3 came into being. This represented an improved *Castle* with a more comprehensive weapon fit. Sadly, as this design tended towards that of a low

PLATE 6.6   The Royal Netherlands Navy *Wolf* class patrol vessel HMNlS *Panter*
(*Photo: Royal Netherlands Navy*)

capability frigate, it was killed off for fear that it might compete for money with the frigate force, or, even worse, be counted as a frigate within the Government's authorised number of frigates for the Royal Navy. This would have reduced the number of genuine blue waterfrigates allowed. After this, there was no return to the *Castle* class, so the two original vessels stand alone with no successors.

CONCLUSION

Modern requirements have caused the offshore tapestry area to be of great significance to nations. There are now many tasks that must be undertaken both in peace and in war and the vessels and their crews that perform them must be able to carry them out in all weathers. The vessels are also required to have a high level of reliability, so that they can spend a high proportion of their time at sea. This situation is not achieved by the use of older 'blue water' frigates or mine-warfare forces.

The OPV design established on a hull derived from a robust, but less sophisti-cated, commercial design can cope with the majority of the offshore tapestry requirements. Depending on the range of tasks that the vessel is required to carry out, the armament of an OPV can either be a simple 40 mm gun, as in the *Island* class, or a range of gun, missile, electronic warfare and helicopter weapons, as in some of the modern designs.

Radar-fitted fixed-wing aircraft have a role in the offshore tapestry area where they can save the OPV much fruitless search time by directing it to areas of more profitable activity. But in peacetime, the prime activity of the OPV in its area is to be the policeman on the beat and this task cannot be done by an aircraft. Helicopters are very valuable in assisting the OPV but they are an expensive addi-tion. Development of the airship may make it capable of some of the OPV's roles, but it suffers from not being on the sea alongside its task.

With growing pressures on Defence expenditure, larger navies are likely to be reluctant to invest in new OPVs. However, interest from smaller navies ensures that there are a number of new OPV designs on the market at present, together with ideas for new concepts in OPV hull design for the future.

7

Mine Warfare: An Introduction

Mines have always played a significant, often devastating role in naval warfare, out of all proportion both to the measures needed to counter them and to the priority given to such measures in peacetime planning and procurement. History abounds with examples of the decisive impact of mining on naval operations, and of the inadequate resources available to otherwise well equipped and prepared navies to deal with it effectively. Even if no mines have actually been laid, the mere claim to have done so constitutes a substantial and very real threat.

THE NATURE OF MINE WARFARE

Mines have been used to disrupt shipping almost since there were navies. They are used either offensively or defensively, that is either to attack an enemy's vessels in areas where they are expected to operate, or to protect one's own naval installations from interference by enemy ships or submarines. They may be laid overtly or covertly, from ships, submarines or aircraft. During the Second World War, some 500,000 mines were laid in all, and were responsible for sinking or damaging more ships than any other weapon. General MacArthur's landing at Inchon during the Korean War almost failed because of mining by the North Koreans, using a makeshift force of junks, while during the Vietnam War, the Americans effectively closed Haiphong and paralysed supply lines for 300 days, initially laying just 36 mines by air. Large multinational MCM forces have been assembled on several recent occasions to deal with what turned out to be very small numbers of mines, for instance in the Suez Canal in 1984, and in the Iran–Iraq war in 1987, when Kuwaiti-flagged oil tankers were the main target.

In the most recent Gulf conflict, the Iraqis admitted to having laid over 1200 mines, a number later officially estimated to be nearer 2500. Both moored and more sophisticated ground mines were used. Clearing channels through the Iraqi minefields was vital to the naval operation, and this task was led by the Royal Navy's *Hunt* class vessels; two of these ships were given the privilege of leading the Coalition naval forces into Al Shu'aybah and Kuwait City, by which time at least 200 mines had been cleared, and over 1000 more identified.

Although they are generally of more up to date construction, the world's current stocks of mines still comprise mainly the familiar 'spiked' contact mine, in use tethered just below the water's surface. They remain quite remarkably effective, as has been clearly demonstrated in even the most recent conflicts, in the Middle East, Vietnam and the Falkland Islands. Modern technology, however, has allowed the development of mines which can remain on the sea-bed to await the precise preprogrammed circumstances, in terms of time of day or year, and type or density of shipping before activation, and to be triggered not by contact but by the various influences which ships inevitably create. Apart from conventional, high explosive mines, there are those which release a torpedo to pursue their quarry, and some which rely on rocket propulsion or other forms of mobility to achieve advantage over their intended targets.

Such sophistication is, of course, also to be seen in the evolution of mine countermeasures (MCM). Tethered or moored mines have traditionally been swept, using mechanical sweep gear towed by a minesweeper. Influence generating sweeps are also in widespread use to counter influence mines on the sea-bed, but this approach is unable to keep pace with advances in mine sophistication. Minesweeping has therefore tended to give way to the more recently developed techniques of minehunting, in which highly specialised vessels and equipment are deployed to find and dispose of individual mines, one by one. These specialised MCM vessels are also very expensive, and navies can generally not afford them in the quantities that are really required; for some types of operation, such as route survey, other, less costly means are perfectly adequate, and in many ways complementary.

In naval mine warfare the disparity between weapon and countermeasure, characteristic of many aspects of warfare, is particularly marked, and is likely to increase as developments in technology continue to be applied both to mines and to the techniques for dealing with them. Despite the preponderance of effort devoted to mine countermeasures, this imbalance seems most unlikely ever to be redressed; this is reflected to some extent in the relative emphasis given to the two sides of the subject in this book, which, after the chapter on mines and minelaying, concentrates on the many and varied aspects of MCM, before bringing the threads together again in the final chapters covering command and control, and possible future developments.

TYPES OF MINE WARFARE OPERATION

In view of the enormous significance of mine warfare, it must of necessity form an integral part in operational planning and execution. Mining may form an essential component of both defensive and offensive operations, and will need to be planned accordingly. This will include the method and timing of laying and activating minefields, and any need to maintain or supplement the initial lay. It is also important that friendly units be kept fully informed of all known mining in their area of operation.

In certain circumstances, appropriate countermeasures operations may be prerequisite to other offensives, although this need may not become evident until the first ship falls prey to a mine. One of the most important considerations will be the suitability of the area for either mining or MCM. In regions of high underwater currents, for instance, mines may well drift from their initial positions; where the sea-bed is very rocky, on the other hand, mines may be virtually impossible for the available MCM capability to detect or deal with. Operational planning, therefore, should be expected to revolve around routes or areas which have been chosen as much for their suitability for mine warfare as for any other operational expedient. MCM efforts can then be concentrated on these designated routes and areas, and units can be readily kept updated on their current condition.

This dependence on predefined routes tends to dominate peacetime activities. In the event of a mine threat being suspected in a given area of operations, a process of route surveillance will normally be carried out, with the aim of confirming or otherwise the extent of the threat. This process will be very much more effective if the results of the surveillance can be compared with the state of the route when it was known that no mines were there. This, then, gives rise to the peacetime activity of route survey, which both identifies the routes needed in support of planned or possible operations and provides an up to date survey of those routes in order to expedite the detection of mines at a later date.

In the event that route surveillance confirms the existence of mines, there are several options available. One is to instigate clearance operations, in order to render the route safe, or safer, for friendly shipping to use, but this can be extremely time consuming. Another option will be to find an alternative route, either from those which may have been planned for such a contingency, or, if necessary, from scratch. Should it not prove feasible to clear or find a sufficiently wide channel for other shipping, quite possibly because of shortage of time, then an MCM vessel may be called upon to escort ships through whatever channel has been cleared, and this is known as a lead-through operation.

8
Mines, Mining and Minelaying

There is considerable similarity between mines and torpedoes; indeed one of the earliest examples of the sea mine was actually a form of torpedo, which, in 1777, was floated down the Delaware river against British ships at anchor. Mines subsequently developed into the familiar, static device which is set to lie in wait for its target to pass or make contact. More recently, however, there has been a definite convergence once more with the torpedo, and many companies nowadays manufacture both types of weapon.

TYPES OF MINE

The most common type of mine, used extensively in both World Wars, is the moored contact mine, tethered to a sinker, and with protruding spikes or horns, which cause detonation on contact. They would thus normally be moored just below the surface, but may be much deeper if submarines are the intended target. Many countries still possess large stocks of these mines, some dating back to the First World War, and they have been encountered most recently in the Persian Gulf and the Red Sea. A small number were used by the Argentinians around Port Stanley and swept very effectively by the Royal Navy after the main hostilities in the Falkland Islands, with considerable assistance from what turned out to be quite reliable records of the minefields captured earlier in the conflict.

In the Second World War, magnetic sensing mines were introduced by Germany. Fortunately, one was recovered intact early on by the British, and its method of operation analysed; appropriate countermeasures were then put into effect. Later in that war, pressure sensing mines were introduced, and used by both sides. These early influence sensors were fairly simple, and of limited effectiveness. A significant improvement was the later introduction of the acoustic sensor, which allowed not only greater range of target detection, but also the potential for discriminating different types of target. A modern influence mine will combine all three methods of detection, using the target's acoustic signature initially and, at closer range and to assist in discerning the type of vessel and possibly its closest point of approach, its pressure and magnetic signatures. Such mines will normally also be ground mines, that is they will simply lie on the sea-bed, rather than being moored; they are thus simpler to lay, and can pack a larger quantity of explosive, although they will not be effective in more than 200 metres or so of water, whereas moored mines could still be used to some effect in much deeper water.

There are other aspects to the increasing sophistication of the modern mine. In

51

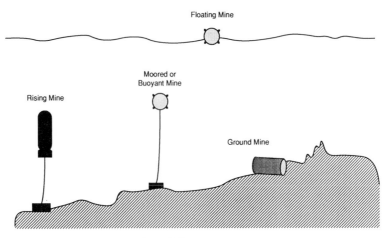

Fig. 8.1   Different Types of Mine

addition to the capability to discriminate vessel type and perhaps behaviour, a ship count may be included, which would, for instance, increase the mine's potency against convoys by allowing a number of escort vessels to pass unharmed and then attacking the more valuable merchant ships being escorted. Timers can also be used to control the mine so that it is not permanently active, but only when a particular type of activity is anticipated, or only after a predetermined period of dormancy. Such techniques make sweeping of the mines very much more difficult or uncertain, and also assist in conserving the mine's own power supplies, which is in itself a growing problem for the mine designer as the complexity of the internal electronics continues to increase.

A typical ground mine is cylindrical in shape, some 2.5 metres in length and half a metre or so in diameter. Most of its volume is taken up with the explosive charge, usually several hundred kilogrammes, but up to 2,400 kilogrammes in some cases. Electronics, sensors and power supplies, together with arming and safety mechanisms, account for the remaining space.

Alternatives to fixed, high explosive mines are becoming more numerous. Mines now exist which can be laid remote from their intended operating positions and then swim to those positions. Mines can also bury themselves in certain types of sea-bed in order to render themselves less susceptible to countermeasures. It is also possible for mines to move after detection, and selection, of a target, either by rising, unguided, to intercept it, or by moving under power, the most well known example of this type being the US Captor (Captive Torpedo) mine, which releases a Mark 46 Torpedo to attack its chosen target. Rocket propelled mines are yet another realistic possibility. As was suggested at the start of this chapter, the division between mine and torpedo is once again very unclear.

PLATE 8.1   The *Stonefish* ground mine (*Photo: Marconi*)

PLATE 8.2   *Sea Urchin* Exercise Variant (*Photo: BAeSEMA*)

Mines for Training Purposes

Many navies are increasingly making use of non-warstock mines for training, exercises and data gathering. Assessment mines can be laid to gather information on a potential enemy's vessels, particularly their various signatures, in order to provide data to be programmed into warstock mines. Similar information on one's own vessels can be used to determine their susceptibility to enemy mines. Recovering data from such mines can be a problem. In friendly waters, cables can be laid, and these can also provide power to the mines, while outside these areas, either the mines themselves need to be recovered or some form of communication link will be needed.

For training and exercise purposes, there are a large range of dummy or inert mines, which can be laid to practise minelaying procedures, and to provide training in certain types of mine countermeasures techniques. Much more useful are the training mines which can simulate a warstock mine by recording all detected activity using pre-programmed sensors and, by means of a simple acoustic link to suitably equipped ships, indicate to such ships when the type of mine being simulated would have detonated. Subsequent recovery of the mine and analysis of its records will reveal every target detected, from which the effectiveness of ships in avoiding or dealing with the minefield can be assessed. A specific example of such a mine, in fairly widespread use, is the British Aerospace Versatile Exercise Mine System (VEMS), which has proved very popular and effective in providing realistic training in mine warfare.

PLATE 8.3   The Versatile Exercise Mine System (*Photo: BAeSEMA*)

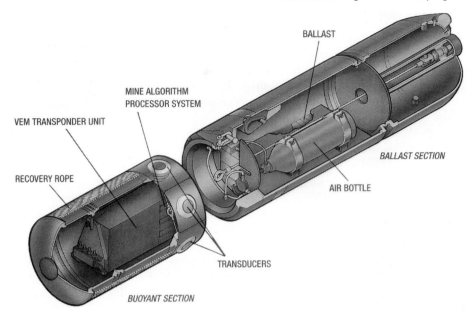

BALLAST

MINE ALGORITHM
PROCESSOR SYSTEM

VEM TRANSPONDER UNIT

BALLAST SECTION

RECOVERY ROPE

AIR BOTTLE

TRANSDUCERS

BUOYANT SECTION

PLATE 8.4   Internal arrangement of the Versatile Exercise Mine System (*Photo: BAeSEMA*)

Minefields

To be effective, mines are laid in minefields, although, as many of the historical examples show, only a small number of mines are needed to cause a major impact on enemy operations. Minefields can be either offensive or defensive in their purpose, but, whatever the intention, must be properly planned to achieve the required effect. This will include determining the type or mix of mines needed, the spacing between them, the depth of water, the type of target and any parameters to be preset, such as target signature data, ship counts, arming delays and activation timings. Another important feature, especially in defensive minefields, will be safe lanes or timings, to allow friendly shipping to pass unhindered. Activation may alternatively be remotely controlled, by cable or acoustic signals, to facilitate such passage.

The concept of a guardian mine is worthy of mention. With the sophistication now available in the mine, it is quite possible to discern target behaviour, and in particular the very distinctive behaviour of mine countermeasures vessels and equipment. Guardian mines could be included in a minefield and targetted at such vessels to deter or neutralise them, leaving the remainder of the minefield undisturbed and still fully able to fulfil its intended purpose.

The potential for communication between mines, by acoustic telemetry for instance, also exists, and could render the minefield an even more potent threat. Target data from several mines could be accumulated to increase confidence in target classification, position and behaviour, or a concerted attack could be made against multiple targets by several mines, thus significantly decreasing the effectiveness of any countermeasures or evasive action taken.

MINELAYING

In general, mines can be laid from almost any type of platform. In defended waters, or where the risk of detection is of lesser importance, overt laying is the norm. Aircraft can be used for speed, although with less accuracy; complex patterns of sowing are also rather difficult to achieve. Surface vessels, of most types, can be used, provided they have the capacity to carry the mines and the mechanics necessary for laying, usually a system of rails. Very few navies, however, maintain vessels dedicated to this purpose, tending instead to rely on converting other vessels, such as Ro-Ro ferries, when the need arises. Covert laying can be achieved by surface vessels, at some risk; more often submarines will be used. Mines can be launched from their torpedo tubes, but this of course reduces the number of tubes immediately available for torpedoes. An alternative is a special mine saddle attached to the submarine's hull, and containing both mines and laying mechanism.

Whichever method is used to lay mines, one important requirement is accurate positioning. The mines must be laid as precisely as possible where planned, if the full effectiveness of the minefield is not to be compromised. Furthermore, the actual lay positions should be recorded accurately to allow the minefield's actual effectiveness to be assessed, to permit subsequent checking for drift of the mines, and to facilitate eventual clearance of the minefield. As is discussed later, the sort of accuracy required is normally available on Mine Countermeasures vessels, but these tend to be otherwise unsuitable for minelaying, due to the space required for the mines themselves. Most other vessels are likely to need additional navigational equipment if they are to function adequately as minelayers. Such equipment could easily form part of a modification package kept available to fit to suitable ships when needed.

9

Minecountermeasures

Minecountermeasures, or MCM, covers any technique or procedure used to deal with mines or the threat of them. There are, of course, measures which are applicable to all vessels and units but the emphasis here is mainly on the platforms and techniques dedicated to the purpose, and the organisations responsible for their conduct and operation. This chapter, therefore, outlines the basic concepts, which are then expanded in the chapters which follow.

In general, specialised MCM platforms are either Minehunters or Minesweepers, in some cases both, and are deployed against a known or suspected mine threat. In the absence of any such threat, however, considerable efforts are committed to survey and surveillance activities in carefully selected areas in order to facilitate detection of any subsequent mining and to build up the extensive databases which are vital to the efficient prosecution of any necessary mine clearance operations.

MINESWEEPING

Minesweeping has been the traditional and, until the advent of Minehunting in the 1970's, the principal approach to clearing mines. Indeed, MCM vessels still tend to be popularly known as Minesweepers even though they may actually be Minehunters.

Minesweeping entails simply passing through the area to be cleared while dragging a suitable device or apparatus designed to detonate mines that may lie in its path. This may be a purely mechanical sweep, which cuts the moorings of moored mines, or some form of influence generator configured to emulate the mines' intended targets. Although these techniques are still very effective against the many older mine types, they are no match for the more discerning and intelligent mines now available.

There are further disadvantages to minesweeping. In general, sweep gear can be deployed from a single vessel to only a limited depth, although deep sweeping is possible by two (or more) vessels operating as a team. In either case, however, once the gear is deployed, it is necessary to maintain considerable speed, normally some 8–12 knots, to ensure that the sweep remains in its intended configuration, and this is particularly critical for the more complex arrangements sometimes used. Manoeuvrability is thus substantially restricted, and a limiting factor in confined areas.

MINEHUNTING

To counter the threat of more sophisticated mines which are not amenable to conventional sweeping, the technique of minehunting has come into use. In essence this means searching out and dealing with every object in the area to be cleared which is, or at least could be, a mine. Searching is most usually carried out with a minehunting sonar, operating at frequencies up to several hundred kilohertz, in order to achieve the necessary resolution. Such sonars are effective only at short ranges, up to, say, one mile, and so, to ensure sufficient time to react to the detection of a possible mine, the vessel must proceed at very low speed, usually no more than about three knots, and often much less. Dealing with a suspected mine will require further reduction in speed or, more likely, a complete stop, and so the overall speed of advance when minehunting may be as low as one knot.

Early minehunting sonars were hull-mounted, with the transducer in some form of dome under the ship. These sonars are effective in depths down to only about 100 metres. Later sonars are of the variable depth type, with the transducers suspended below the vessel in a towed body. As well as giving increased depth capability, this also gives a better profile of targets on the sea-bed, as should be clear from Figure 9.1.

The actual process of prosecuting a minelike item divides into four main stages:

▶ *Detection*—of the initial evidence of a possible mine's existence, followed by

▶ *Classification*—to determine the likelihood of the item being a mine, confirmation depending upon

▶ *Identification*—of the actual type of mine, followed by

▶ *Disposal*—or removal of the mine from the area.

The process stops at Classification for sonar contacts classified as non-mine. Details of such items should, nonetheless, be accurately recorded to assist in any future MCM operations in the area.

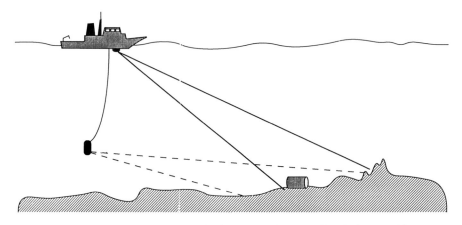

Fig. 9.1   A variable depth sonar will give a much better profile of a bottom object

Only the first two stages of the minehunting process are, in any case, within the capabilities of most minehunting sonars. Identification usually requires some form of visual contact, and will result in determination of significant details of the mine, including size, type—eg pressure, magnetic, Captor and so on—, type and quantity of explosive, etc. Disposal can be accomplished in several ways— neutralisation, countermining, physical removal from the area and so forth. Identification and disposal of mines was traditionally the role of the Mine Clearance Diver, deployed from the MCM ship in a dinghy. Nowadays both tasks can be effectively and much more safely carried out with a remotely controlled vehicle, of which there are many different types available. Such vehicles can be equipped with low-light television, high definition sonar, cutters to deal with moored mines and mine disposal charges for countermining. It is of interest to note, however, that many of the mines identified by the remotely controlled vehicles in the Gulf War were actually disposed of by charges placed by divers.

Throughout these latter stages of mine prosecution, the MCM vessel must stand off at such a distance from the mine that it can maintain sonar contact and be within the operating range of the remotely controlled vehicle, while remaining sufficiently far away for safety reasons. With the increasingly effective ranges of mines, and the prospect of the MCM platform itself being a specific target for certain types of mine, the stand off distance for acceptable safety can exceed the required operating radius by a considerable margin. To ensure adequate safety levels in these circumstances it is necessary for rather more of the process to be carried out by remotely controlled vehicles, and a new generation of these is now emerging to provide for this need. They also open up the possibility of being operated from almost any platform, rather than dedicated MCM vessels, which affords much greater operational flexibility.

ROUTE SURVEY AND SURVEILLANCE

The minehunter's task will be considerably facilitated if it is already aware of those items it can expect to detect, but which are known, from previous MCM operations or otherwise, not to be mines. This obviates the need to spend further time or effort in reclassifying them. These objects are often known as NOMBOS (NOn-Mine Bottom ObjectS). It is one of the aims of peacetime Route Survey to provide as much information of this sort as possible for use in possible clearance operations. This information is often promulgated in the form of a Mine Warfare Pilot (see Chapter 12). Route Survey itself can be carried out using sector scanning sonar, as if minehunting, but, even though no mines are expected to be encountered, progress will still be comparatively slow if adequate coverage is to be achieved. Greater speed is possible, up to 10 knots or so, by using a side-scanning sonar linked to a suitable recorder, which will yield what resembles an aerial photograph of the swath covered. Any suspicious or unknown contacts revealed on analysis of the records can then be specifically investigated, as can any differences between successive surveys, which might well provide early indication of mining activity. This would then be regarded as Route Surveillance.

 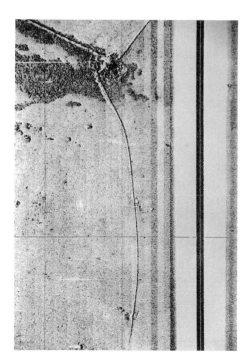

PLATE 9.1   (Left) Typical Sidescan Sonar records. This shows a cylindrical mine about one metre in length, with the acoustic shadow behind. In front of this is a trench, with the shadow at the nearer edge to the transducer. (*Photo: DMOS*)

PLATE 9.2   (Right) This shows the three cables of a mooring buoy, and a moored mine, at the bottom edge, attached to one of the cables. The unensonified swath immediately below the transducer is also clearly shown at the right of the photograph. (*Photo: DMOS*)

GENERAL REQUIREMENTS FOR MCM

From the foregoing outline of the various types of MCM operations, certain of the essential requirements for command and control should be evident. One feature of all MCM operations is the dependence on predetermined straight routes, chosen both to suit the needs of other operations and for their suitability for MCM. It is important to have available as much information as possible on these routes, not just their positions, but the depth of water, type of sea-bed, navigational difficulties, and so on, as well as the results of all previous MCM effort in the area. This information requires careful management, particularly in maintaining it as operations proceed. It is also characteristic of MCM operations that, notwithstanding the rate of progress likely to be achieved, they are extremely intensive, and place considerable demands on the crews involved. Vessels must therefore be appropriately tasked, not only to make optimum use of their particular capabilities in the area concerned, but also to maintain their effectiveness over a protracted period. The progress of a task also needs to be monitored, and the plans updated accordingly, much as in any other type of operation.

As far as the vessels themselves are concerned, as well as deploying the various systems and equipments required, and handling the not insignificant amount of data involved, there is a substantial requirement for accurate navigation, in order to minimise the uncertainties in the actual coverage achieved and in any subsequent relocation of sonar contacts requiring further investigation or other action. It is also necessary for the platforms to maintain straight tracks (over the sea-bed) in order to minimise the overlap needed with parallel paths to ensure adequate coverage. When minesweeping this must be done while towing the sweeps, which can significantly affect ship control, while for minehunting, the speeds are usually very low, sometimes, especially with an unfavourable tide, below the threshold for maintaining steerage. A further requirement in minehunting is to be able to hover the ship over a fixed point on the sea-bed to allow prosecution of a mine. These various requirements are discussed in more detail in the following chapters.

10
Platforms for MCM

The general requirements for a MCM platform have already been indicated in the previous chapter. Clearly the platform must permit the specialised sensors and other systems to be deployed in and around possible minefields, while keeping the risks to the safety of the platform and its crew to an acceptable minimum. Mention has also been made of the need for precise, slow-speed manoeuvring control for a minehunter, and of the requirement for a minesweeper to deploy, tow and recover its sweep gear. The platform, furthermore, must be able to withstand the high degree of shock which may result from a mine detonating close by.

MINIMISING RISK

To minimise the risk of the MCM vessel itself becoming a target for the mines it has set out to counter, it is necessary that its detectable signatures, specifically acoustic, magnetic and pressure, should be considerably lower than those normally exhibited by warships. This represents an essential requirement in the design of the vessel, and numerous specialised techniques have been employed in this regard. Special care needs to be given to the mountings for noisy equipment—engines, generators and so on—and, of course, to the hull and propulsion designs to minimise motion acoustics.

Magnetic signature is kept down by the use, wherever possible, of non-magnetic materials, even for very small components such as nuts and bolts, and particularly for moving parts and portable items. It is normal also to fit a degaussing system to the vessel to compensate for the inevitable residual magnetic signature. By rigorous application of these principles the overall magnetic signature of the Royal Navy's *Hunt* class ships was reduced by a factor of some 250 when compared with the use of conventional warship construction techniques.

As far as reduction of pressure signature is concerned, at least for conventional hulls, it is really only in the area of the design of the hull itself that there is any scope, with such hulls tending to be fairly flat-bottomed and of shallow draught. Alternative types of hull, however, are gaining in popularity, and are covered later on.

CONSTRUCTION MATERIALS

One of the longest running debates in the field of platform design concerns the material to be used for the hull. The venerable 'Ton' class, designed in the early

1950s, is of wooden construction, with an aluminium frame. Although many are still in service around the world, maintenance is expensive, and the hull's shock resistance is limited. In the 1960s, therefore, attention was switched to using glass reinforced plastic (GRP), and the first such ship, HMS *Wilton*, which copied the *Ton* class design, was completed in 1973. This proved highly successful, and was followed by the *Hunt* class Minehunter/sweeper, of which 13 are now in service with the Royal Navy. Many other navies have followed this lead in using GRP, although there are, naturally, differences of opinion as to the optimum construction methods, and much has been written in support or otherwise of the various options available. Suffice it to say that tests, including measurements taken on board HMS *Brecon*, the first of the *Hunt* class, when she sailed for the first time into a Force 10 gale, have proved beyond doubt the outstanding shock resistance and inherent strength of a GRP hull. One other material, however, deserves a mention, and that is amagnetic steel, currently favoured by the German Navy, and being used for their Type 343 fast minelayer/minesweeper class. This material offers slight advantages over non-conductive materials in terms of earth bonding and electromagnetic interference amongst equipments, but does require very careful quality control in its manufacture and handling. Many other factors, such as fire resistance, acoustic transmissivity, susceptibility to corrosion and so on, are relevant, and will continue to fuel the debate over construction material for many years yet, it would seem.

PROPULSION

Propulsion is the other area of major interest. Diesel engines are commonly used, albeit designed with reduced magnetic signature in mind, and mounted so as to minimise transmission of noise to the hull. For slow speeds, electric propulsion is preferred for the better control it offers. The *Hunt* class, for instance, has three diesels, two for main drive, through conventional screws, for transit and minesweeping, and one to supply power for the electric slow-speed drive and for certain auxiliary needs, such as winches. To provide the precise control and manoeuvrability needed for minehunting, many different propulsion configurations are available, including 'active' rudders, which comprise small propellers on the outboard edges of the rudders, additional thrusters, which may be outboard, or fitted into the hull, usually at the bows, and the highly versatile cycloidal propellers, or Voith Schneiders, which can be controlled to exert thrust in any direction. A pair of these propellers will suffice for most purposes, taking the place of conventional screws and rudders. The Royal Navy's new *Sandown* class of Single Role Minehunter (SRMH) is so equipped, but also has bow thrusters, whose use, however, is restricted in order to minimise the acoustic interference they might cause to the minehunting sonar. Some examples of propulsion systems are shown in Plates 10.1 and 10.2 and Figure 10.1. The business of controlling the propulsion system to achieve the precise positioning necessary is left until a later chapter.

However careful the design of the platform and its installed equipment, its signature levels will inevitably change, as equipment characteristics alter with time and use, and systems are modified or replaced. Regular monitoring is therefore essential to ensure optimum performance. For this purpose, acoustic and

PLATE 10.1   HMS *Sandown* turning. (*Photo: Vosper Thorneycroft*)

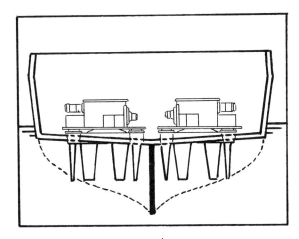

FIG. 10.1   The arrangement of the two Voith Schneider propellers in the Swedish
Landsort class

magnetic ranges are needed, through which the ships pass to measure their signature levels. The importance of this is illustrated by the fact that, for the Gulf conflict, the Royal Navy actually deployed mobile ranging systems in the Gulf in support of its considerable MCM efforts, in order to ensure that the signatures of the ships could be maintained at the necessary low levels during the course of the operation.

ALTERNATIVE HULL DESIGNS

Although the majority of the world's MCM vessels are of a conventional single displacement hull design, the various special requirements of such platforms have led to the use, or at least the consideration, of numerous other platform types. An obvious choice might seem to be the air cushion vehicle, or hovercraft, which has virtually no pressure signature and a very high resistance to underwater shock. It can also move at comparatively high speeds, which is useful for transiting to and from operational areas, and a significant advantage over more conventional designs, which are not generally capable of more than about 15 knots. There are, however, difficulties in deploying and operating specialised MCM systems, particularly sonars, from hovercraft, and the general platform reliability and maintenance overheads are of the same order as those associated with airframes. Although hovercraft have been trialled as MCM platforms, they have not been seriously taken up in this role.

A variation on the hovercraft theme, which retains most of the advantages, but few of the disadvantages, has been adopted by the Royal Norwegian Navy for a class of Minehunters and Minesweepers currently under development. These vessels will be twin-hulled surface effect ships (SES), which have rigid sidewalls but ride on an air cushion, their design being based on Norway's considerable experience of building ferries using the SES principle. A similar approach by the

PLATE 10.2   The value of GRP for MCM ships was first established by HMS
Wilton (*Photo: VT*)

PLATE 10.3   HMS *Ledbury*, the Royal Navy's second generation GRP mine-
hunter/sweeper. The minehunting sight can be seen on the bridge roof in front of
the radar. (*Photo: VT*)

US Navy, the ill-fated *Cardinal* class, foundered, not because of the unconven-
tional design, but because of difficulties and inexperience in the US in the use of
GRP as a hull material.

Displacement hull catamaran designs have also found some favour, the French
BAMO class currently under construction being one such example. The Royal
Australian Navy's *Bay* class is also of such a type, the first, HMAS *Rushcutter*,
having been laid down in 1986. This design is of particular interest in that the
weapon system is fitted in a container, mounted on the after deck, and which can
be removed to allow for fault rectification or possibly a change of role. This concept is also applied to the Danish *Stanflex* ships, for which various different
weapon system modules are available, allowing rapid reconfiguration as a
patrol boat, missile boat, MCM craft or Minelayer. This is discussed further in
Chapter 18.

One other twin hull form, the SWATH, or Small Waterplane Area Twin Hull,

PLATE 10.4 HMS *Cromer*, the third of the Royal Navy's *Sandown* class
(*Photo: VT*)

PLATE 10.5 The US Navy's *Avenger*, a large ocean-going minehunter, with a
significant fighting capability in addition to her MCM role. (*Photo: Marconi*)

design has yet to be taken up, although some shipbuilders have made proposals
for such craft.

Although an MCM vessel might typically be only 50–60 metres in length, dis-
placing some 500–700 tons, meeting the stringent requirements for reduced signatures and precise manoeuvrability makes them comparatively very expensive to
produce, and so it is scarcely surprising that more economic alternatives have been
considered. Using remotely controlled craft, thus obviating the need for the control vessel itself to be capable of operating close to the mines, is one such option,
exemplified by the German Navy's *Troika* system, which comprises a control, or

PLATE 10.6   The SAM remotely controlled sweep platform, up to three of which can be controlled by one *Landsort* vessel of the Royal Swedish Navy (*Photo: Karlskrona Varvet*)

PLATE 10.7   *Tripartite* MCMVs of the Royal Netherlands Navy. The *Tripartite* is the result of a highly successful international collaboration. A number are also operated by the other two participants, Belgium and France. (*Photo: GNM*)

mother, ship, which as it happens are converted *Lindau* class minesweepers, and three much smaller craft. These small operating vessels can take a crew of three, for transit purposes, and set them up for a MCM task, after which they are operated unmanned and controlled by radio and radar tracking from the mother ship. Another example of this technique is the Swedish SAM remotely controlled minesweeping catamarans, up to three of which can be controlled from a *Landsort* class MCM vessel. More recently, much smaller remotely operated vehicles (ROV) have been taking on increased MCM capability in their own right, opening up the realistic prospect of their being deployed directly from warships or merchant vessels rather than specialised MCMVs; this is covered in more detail in a later chapter.

No navy has sufficient vessels to meet its MCM needs, and not only because of the high cost of their procurement. To make up the shortfall it is possible, in times of need, to make use of other suitable craft for certain purposes. There are clear similarities between minesweepers and stern trawlers, for instance, and these latter, with only minor modification, are likely to be quite well suited to sweeping simple moored mines. This was amply demonstrated by the Royal Navy when it commissioned five trawlers into the fleet for the Falklands campaign. These temporary minesweepers were used to prepare the routes for the landings by the Task Force, and one of them had the doubtful privilege of bringing a recovered Argentinian mine all the way back to the UK for analysis.

Yet another approach is the so-called COOP, or Craft Of OPportunity, concept, which originated in the US. This is intended to facilitate Route Survey, by fitting a comparatively simple set of equipment, basically comprising a towed sidescan sonar, a data recorder and a navigation system, to any small craft which may be available. This again was put into practice by the Royal Navy during the Gulf conflict, when a survey launch was so equipped, while on passage to the Gulf, the equipment later being transferred to the survey ship itself.

AIRBORNE MCM

Finally in this brief review of MCM platforms mention must be made of airborne MCM, of which the US Navy is both the principal practitioner, and, by virtue of the lack of attention given to maintaining its surface MCM fleet over the last 20 years or so, almost totally reliant for any credible off-shore MCM capability. It has a fleet of Sikorsky *Sea Stallion* helicopters which can tow a sled configured either with magnetic or acoustic sweeps, or with sidescanning sonar for rapid route survey. Plans are underway to upgrade to *Sea Dragon* helicopters, which have a much greater lift potential, with the aim of having 35 of these aircraft in service by 1996. There are obvious limitations in the use of helicopters, particularly in terms of their capacity to carry the necessary navigation, data processing and control equipment, and to provide power or fuel for the towed equipment, and of their endurance on task and the need for specialised support facilities; there are, on the other hand, major advantages in their immunity to the effects of mines and in their inherent speed, both on task and in transit, and they have proven effective in use, in the Persian Gulf, for instance, clearing mines laid to disrupt oil traffic during the Iran–Iraq war.

11

Minesweeping and Minehunting

MECHANICAL SWEEPING

The traditional approach to clearing mines is minesweeping, whereby a minesweeper simply passes through the area to be cleared dragging an apparatus designed to dispose of any mines in its path. Against moored mines a mechanical sweep, to a design substantially unchanged since World War I, is often used. This comprises one or two wires deployed behind and to one or both sides of the minesweeper, and kept at a constant depth and in the required disposition by means of attached floats, diverters and depressors. Along the wires are affixed cutters, either mechanical or explosive in operation, to cut the mooring of any mine caught by the sweep. The widely used Oropesa wire sweep is shown in Figure 11.1.

For deeper mechanical sweeping it is usually necessary to use two or more vessels, working as a team, with the sweep wire arranged between them. The Royal Navy's Deep Armed Team Sweep system, which is operated by the new *River* class minesweepers, is shown at Figure 11.2. This can be used to sweep almost at sea-bed level. With all such wire sweep systems, however, a significant problem is that of maintaining a constant height or depth, since this depends on many factors, particularly the speed of the sweep through the water. Recent research has been aimed at providing equipment to monitor or even control the performance of these sweeps by, for instance, dynamically adjusting vessel speed and cable length.

When a moored mine has been released by minesweeping, if it has not already exploded, it will rise to the surface. The traditional way of disposing of floating mines, such as these, is by gunfire. This was found unreliable by the Royal Navy in the Persian Gulf, mainly because some of the mines tended to sink rather than explode, and so remained a hazard. A special remotely controlled disposal vehicle, known as *Scarab*, and shown in Plate 11.1, was therefore developed by the UK's Admiralty Research Establishment (ARE). *Scarab* can be manoeuvred up to a floating mine, grab hold of it, and then move away, leaving its grab around the mine and on a tether. The mine can then be detonated by remote command, if necessary after having been towed by *Scarab* to a safer area.

INFLUENCE SWEEPING

To sweep influence mines, various forms of towed influence generators exist. A fairly rudimentary form of acoustic sweep is the pipe noisemaker, which

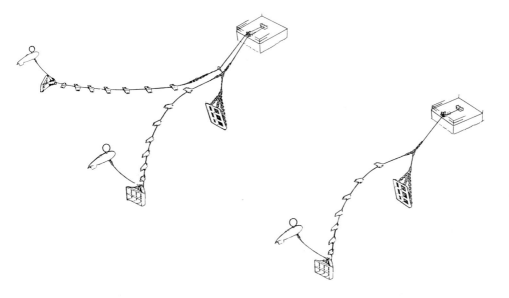

FIG. 11.1   The *Oropesa* wire sweep in single and double configurations

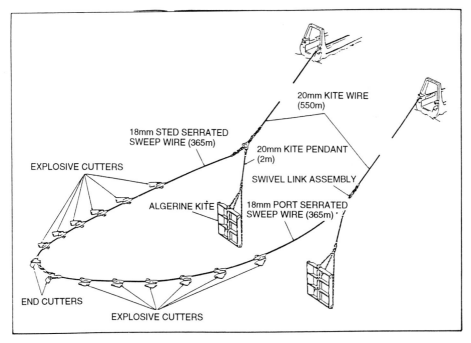

FIG. 11.2   Arrangement of the BAJ *Extra Deep Armed Team Sweep* (EDATS) or
Wire Sweep Mk. 9 This is the sweep gear used by the Royal Navy's *River* class MSFs

PLATE 11.1   The *Scarab* mine disposal unit, used to deal with risen or floating mines. The grab arms are visible in the raised position at the front. (*Photo: Maritime Defence*)

PLATE 11.2   The *Towed Acoustic Generator* (TAG) and 3-ton davit aboard the *Hunt* class MCMV HMS *Brecon* (*Photo: Vosper Thorneycroft*)

comprises simply an arrangement of pipes tied together and dragged along the sea-bed. This has some fairly obvious limitations, and a rather better known and more effective acoustic sweep is the *Osborn* system, used by the Royal Navy (see Plates 11.2, 11.3, 11.4 and Fig 11.3). This system consists of a noise generator, weighing some two and a half tons, towed on a cable which also supplies the power needed, a towed monitor hydrophone, and the on-board control equipment. The noise generator is essentially a huge loudspeaker, driven by the control system on the towing vessel to create sound at a range of frequencies and amplitudes, which have been programmed to simulate the requisite target characteristics. The system

PLATE 11.3   The *Towed Acoustic Generator* (TAG) of *MSSA1* (*Photo: BAeSEMA*)

PLATE 11.4   The *Towed Acoustic Monitor* (TAM) (*Photo: BAeSEMA*)

can be operated in the open loop mode, with just the generator deployed, or with the monitor also in use to give closed loop control. As well as the noise levels actually generated, the depths and the distances behind the ship of the two units are critical from both a safety and an effectiveness point of view, since sufficient noise must be generated to influence mines in a wide enough swath for the exercise to be worthwhile, but not to the extent that mines are influenced so far in front of the sweep as to endanger the minesweeper itself. These critical parameters must be measured continuously to allow both swept pathwidth and the degree of risk to the ship to be assessed and monitored.

To create a magnetic influence is most commonly done by means of an electric current. A typical magnetic sweep would take the form of a large loop of copper wire, through which a substantial current is pulsed to create a magnetic field. The loop needs to be kept in shape, and afloat, and, as for any towed sweep, well behind the ship for safety reasons. Current levels of typically 2000 amps are used, and so a considerable quantity of electric power must be generated, and only limited control over the type of signature created is likely to be available.

It is possible to use more than one type of sweep at a time in order to generate a more comprehensive signature. Such an arrangement is known as a Combined Influence Sweep (CIS). The difficulties inherent in deploying, towing and recovering the many hundreds of metres of towed cable and the various diverse attachments associated with just one type of sweep are significantly magnified when using a CIS, and may prove to be somewhat out of proportion to the increase in minesweeping effectiveness achieved.

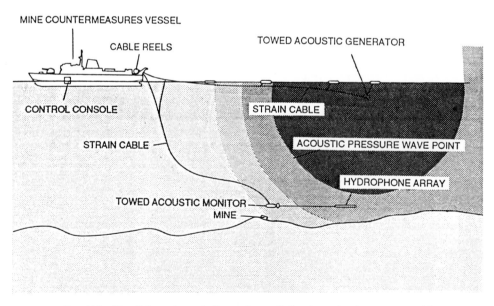

Fig. 11.3   The *Osborn Acoustic Sweep System* [Mine Sweeping System Acoustic]
(MSSA Mk I)

THE VARIABLE MOMENT MAGNET SYSTEM

The techniques described so far have been in use for very many years and, although effective against the simpler mines which they were designed to counter, are no equal for the more discriminating types of mine now available. Indeed, few, if any, advances have been made in minesweeping, despite the seemingly relentless progress of mine sophistication; this is largely because the underlying philosophy, of trying to emulate the mine's target's behaviour sufficiently faithfully to ensure that the mine believes that a real target is present, is inevitably limited in its practical realisation, particularly by the need for knowledge of the mine's own characteristics. In the last few years, however, an alternative technique has evolved, known as *Target Sweeping*, in which the emphasis is more on the characteristics of the ships whose safe passage is to be assured. In essence, the minesweeper tows a CIS which reproduces the signatures of the ships to be protected. For safety reasons, several passes would probably be made, and, if no mines detonate, it can be assumed that the ships which have been simulated will themselves be able to effect a safe transit. If, however, some mines are detonated, it is necessary to make sufficient passes to reduce the number of detonations to an acceptably low level.

Although acoustic sweeps have long had the capability to operate in this way, only more recently has it become feasible to achieve the requisite flexibility with a magnetic sweep. This is due to the concept of a *Variable Moment Magnet* (VMM), which originated at the UK's ARE. The VMM is a cylindrical assembly, some five and a half metres in length, and weighing about 2000 kg in air. It comprises 18 magnetic cores, each of which can be driven into magnetic saturation in either direction by means of a solenoid, thus allowing the magnetic moment of the assembly to be set at any desired level. Compared to previous magnetic sweeps, it has the advantages of considerably lower hydrodynamic drag, and substantially reduced electric power requirements, since power is needed only to alter the moment; the resulting field levels are also somewhat lower, but the possibility exists of deploying the system from much smaller vessels.

For effective target sweeping, up to six VMMs may be needed, depending on the complexity of the magnetic signature of the target ship. It is also necessary, of course, to measure the actual signature of the target ship, to be sure that it will be faithfully reproduced by the system, and for this magnetic ranging facilities will be needed.

The VMM system can also be used more as a conventional magnetic sweep, by pulsing the current around the cores to sweep simple magnetic mines. A third possible use would be to use the comparatively simple magnetic signature produced in this way to mask the real signature of a likely target ship. A standard sweep, with several passes, would first be carried out, to ensure that there are no simple magnetic mines, and then the VMMs would be deployed from the target vessel, to generate the same simple sweep signature, such that any mines detecting it would believe it to be that of the minesweeper once again. The different ways of using the VMM system are shown in Figure 11.4.

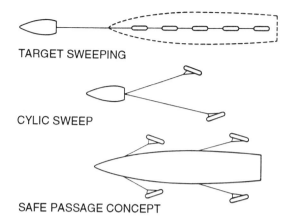

TARGET SWEEPING

CYLIC SWEEP

SAFE PASSAGE CONCEPT

Fig. 11.4   The different towing configurations of the *Variable Moment Magnet System*

AIRBORNE MINESWEEPING

For airborne minesweeping, the US Navy uses sleds towed by *Sea Dragon* or *Sea Stallion* helicopters. Earlier systems comprised either wire sweeps with cutters or non-powered influence sweeps, which were either a cavitating disk in a venturi tube, turned by the flow of the water to generate an acoustic signature, or the *Magnetic Orange Pipe*, a magnetised iron pipe filled with styrofoam. The more up to date *Mk 105* hydrofoil sled, carries its own gas turbine powered generator, which can be refuelled from the towing helicopter, and which provides electric power for a pair of electrodes forming a magnetic sweep. It can also tow the acoustic sweep mentioned above to become the *Mk 106* combined sweep. Both have been used extensively and to good effect in the Persian Gulf and Red Sea mine clearance operations.

MINESWEEPING EFFECTIVENESS

It is important to know the effectiveness of minesweeping, in terms of the swept pathwidth achieved. For mechanical sweeping this is simply the width of the deployed sweeping gear. With influence sweeping more complex calculations are needed, based on the signature levels generated, the signature levels the mines were believed to require for detonation, any complicating factors such as ship counts or other mine intelligence, and the geometry of the sweep itself. The probability of a mine being detonated is also relevant, and formulae have been devised to determine the optimum number of passes over a mine to provide maximum confidence of achieving mine detonation. In general, after only a few passes, the 'point of diminishing returns' is reached, when any further passes will add virtually nothing to the chances of detonating more mines. Equally, if the probability of detonating a mine is, in the first instance, very low, achieving satisfactory coverage is almost impossible, and, in the extreme case where that probability is zero, which means that the sweep is absolutely impotent against that type of mine, then the swept pathwidth will also be zero.

PLATE 11.5   Airborne Minesweeping as practised by the US Navy (*US Navy*)

MINEHUNTING: DETECTION AND CLASSIFICATION

Although other methods, such as magnetic anomaly detection, have been tried, the main sensor equipment for both detection and classification remains the *Minehunting Sonar*. In essence a minehunting sonar consists of a transducer which emits bursts of sound, or 'pings', at an appropriate frequency, in the form of a beam of known geometry. Anything within this beam will be ensonified, and the area of the sea-bed ensonified is known as the 'footprint'. Sound will be reflected and received at the transducer, and it will then be processed by the sonar and presented on a display, which will show some or all of the sonar footprint. The strength of the returned sound will depend upon the range, aspect and nature of whatever reflected it, as well as the environmental conditions, clutter level, reverberation and so on. Prominent objects will be evident both from their echoes and from any acoustic shadow they cast; this shadow can make detection somewhat easier, and also contributes to the classification by allowing the physical dimensions of the object to be estimated. Detection of possible mines is therefore dependent upon the acoustic discrimination between the object and its background, as well as on other factors, including the environment and the skill of the operator. The likelihood of detection is usually expressed as a probability, P_D, the Probability of Detection, and this is a crucial parameter in any operational planning.

To conduct a search it is necessary to cause the footprint to move over the area in such a way that the P_D figure throughout the area is always greater than some predetermined level. With simpler sonars, whose search displays align closely with the actual footprint, the beam is steered, or trained, in a suitable pattern back and forth across the path along which the ship is advancing. More sophisticated sonars can process a much larger footprint, and scan the display over it electronically. In any case, the number of pings striking a point will affect the value of P_D at that point; as a general rule, three pings is regarded as both necessary and sufficient to achieve an optimum figure. In planning a search, special calculations will be needed to determine the searched pathwidth and speed of advance, given the sonar conditions and required value for P_D. The actual formulae used by individual navies, however, tend to be somewhat sensitive, and cannot be given here.

The process of detection gives rise to the suspicion of the presence of a mine-like object, and may occur anywhere out to the maximum effective range of the sonar. Further evidence in support of this hypothesis derives from Classification, for which a more detailed view of the object is required. A higher frequency is therefore used, and at a correspondingly shorter range. Resolution down to around one tenth of a metre is possible under the right conditions, with details such as lifting eyes being discernible. By measuring the size of the object's image, and of any acoustic shadow evident, it is quite possible to get a good estimate of the size of the object itself; indeed more recently sonars have included suitable screen cursors for this purpose, and will provide a direct readout of the dimensions so measured.

From the evidence available, the operator must make a judgement as to whether the object is definitely not a mine, or is possibly or probably a mine. Certainty comes only from Identification, and it is this and the following stage of disposal which are the most time consuming stages of mine prosecution. It will be necessary to proceed to these stages only when a possible or probable mine classification has been given. If the object subsequently proves not to be a mine, this additional effort might have been saved had a more accurate classification been achieved; conversely a mine given a non-mine classification will survive and remain a threat. Classification accuracy depends upon a number of factors, including the sonar's capability in the conditions at the time, and the skill of the operator. As with detection, it is often expressed as a probability, P_{CC}, the Probability of Correct Classification. The higher the P_{CC}, the more effective the minehunter as a whole, since less time will be spent investigating non-mines, and fewer mines will evade the intended scrutiny.

As an example of the significance of the probability figures described above, consider a minefield of 50 mines, in an area also containing 200 other objects which might nonetheless appear to be mines. If $P_D = 0.9$, then 225 of the total 250 minelike objects will be detected. If $P_{CC} = 0.8$, then 180 of these 225 will be correctly classified, leaving 70 of the original 250 either undetected or not identified. In practice, these probability figures would be regarded as fairly good.

The effectiveness of the effort can be enhanced by making several passes over the area, but, as with minesweeping, the benefits rapidly diminish, and, in general, after five passes no further practical benefits can be expected. Planning calculations must, however, provide for multiple passes to achieve acceptable figures, particularly for P_D.

MINEHUNTING SONARS

As regards actual sonars, early examples had a single mechanically trained transducer protruding below the hull of the minehunter, and suitably protected by some form of acoustically transparent dome. This dome and the trunk in which the transducer mechanics operate are filled with sea water, at the appropriate pressure, so that there is no air-water boundary for the sound energy to cross. One of the most widely used and successful of these types of sonar is the *Marconi 193M*, the natural successor to the *193* sonar of the *Ton* class minehunters, and fitted to the Royal Navy's *Hunt* class vessels and those of many other navies too. The *193M* provides two operator displays, for search and classification, as shown in Plates 11.6 and 11.7. With only one single beam transducer, however, detection and classification are almost mutually exclusive, which is a severe limitation, and the classification display shows just a small range window on the same bearing as the search display. The single beam has a maximum detection range of around 600 yards, and can be scanned through a pattern to cover the required sector, or be trained to one side for sidescanning, as indicated at Figure 11.5.

Current generation sonars tend to be of the variable depth variety. Main examples are the *Sonar 2093*, fitted to the Royal Navy's *Sandown* class Single Role Minehunters, and the SQQ 32, used by the US Navy on the *Avenger* class. In these sonars, there are several transducer arrays, mounted in a 'towed body', which can be deployed below the hull on a cable. The *Sonar 2093* towed body can be seen in Plate 11.9. Search scanning is performed electronically, over a beamwidth of perhaps 90 degrees, while a separate array is used for classification, allowing a search to continue uninterrupted; other arrays may be used for side-scan operation, but this is covered in the next chapter on route survey. Once the body has left its stowage position in the hull, or its hull operating position, it becomes necessary to know its frame of reference for both position and heading, since these will no longer be those of the minehunter itself. The towed body therefore carries its own compass, and its position relative to the ship is measured acoustically by means of a short baseline tracking system. The general arrangement is shown at Figure 11.6. Control of the body's depth is also important, to ensure that it is operating close enough to the sea-bed for optimum detection and classification performance, while not being so close that it risks damage, particularly when the vessel changes speed or if the sea-bed is not flat.

Technology is, as yet, unable to offer automatic detection of minelike objects. Although modern sonars do provide a limited degree of computer assistance, responsibility remains with the operator to scan the picture presented to him and mark, probably using some form of cursor, anything he thinks may prove of interest. Further assistance is often available in the form of a picture store, which can hold several views of an object, which might, in practice, be from different aspects, in order to facilitate classification.

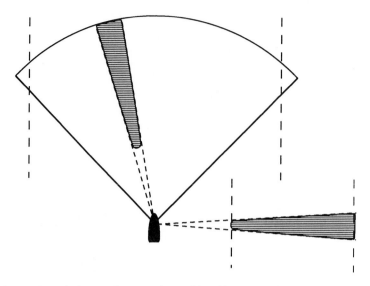

Fig. 11.5   A single sonar beam can be used for either conventional sector scanning, in which it scans back and forth through the defined sector, or for sidescanning, when it would be trained on a fixed bearing to one side or the other. Also shown are the effective limits of sonar coverage in each case

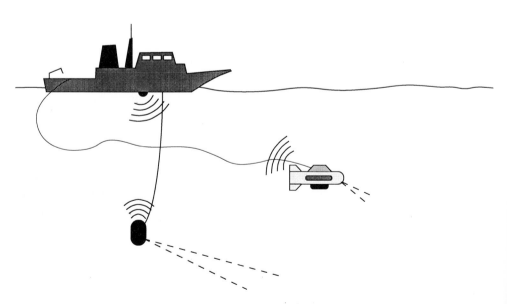

Fig. 11.6   Typical arrangement showing a variable depth sonar and a ROV deployed and both being tracked using a short baseline acoustic tracking system

PLATE 11.6   The operator's console of *Sonar 193M Mod 1* as used by the Royal
Navy and many other navies. The search display is on the left and the classification
display, showing a strong contact in the centre, is on the right. Note also the 'A'
scan display on the right of the classification display (*Photo: Marconi*)

IDENTIFICATION AND DISPOSAL

By the time the classification of a possible or probable mine has been determined, the minehunter may well be only about 200 metres from the contact, and
may even have at least partially circumnavigated it in order to acquire several
different perspectives. To identify it positively as a mine requires visual contact,
and nowadays this is most commonly achieved by means of a remotely operated
vehicle (ROV). In exceptional circumstances, poor underwater visibility, for
instance, it may be necessary to revert to the more traditional approach of send-
ing down a diver. In either case, directing, or conning, the diver or vehicle to the
contact can be tricky. A common practice is to send the diver out in a dinghy,
below which a distinctive sonar reflector is suspended. The dinghy is then directed
from the ship until the sonar reflector appears exactly over the contact on the
sonar display, and the diver then descends. Some minehunters are fitted with a
special 'minehunting sight', which mimics the sonar in azimuth to assist the
dinghy's helmsman. Such a device can be seen above the bridges of both the *Ton*
and *Hunt* Class ships shown earlier. Similarly ROVs normally carry a sonar transponder which will show up clearly on the sonar display. They are also tracked by

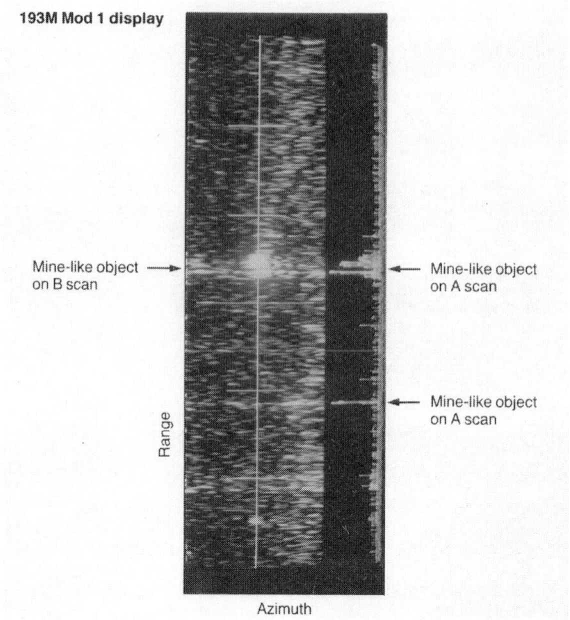

193M Mod 1 display

Mine-like object on B scan →

← Mine-like object on A scan

← Mine-like object on A scan

Range

Azimuth

PLATE 11.7   An example of the classification display of Sonar 193M Mod 1
(*Photo: Marconi*)

PLATE 11.8   The general arrangement of *Sonar 2093* when deployed.
(*Photo: Marconi*)

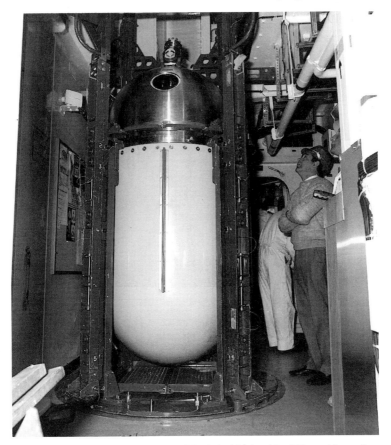

PLATE 11.9   The *Sonar 2093* Towed Body inside the ship. (*Photo: Marconi*)

means of a short baseline acoustic tracking system, just as the towed body of a variable depth sonar is tracked. Control is further facilitated, since the vehicle is steered from the ship's operations room, at a console next to or within sight of the sonar displays, and probably by the same operator. These control facilities can be seen in the operations rooms depicted in Plates 13.1, 13.2, 13.4 and 13.5.

Types of ROV

ROVs can carry a variety of equipment for mine identification and disposal. A low light television camera and searchlight are standard, with the picture displayed at the control console on the ship, to allow for contact identification by the operator. Many vehicles now also carry their own sonar, again with a display on the ship. For mine disposal, the usual arrangement is a mine disposal charge which can be dropped next to the mine. After recovery of the ROV, the charge is detonated by an acoustic signal from the ship. Some ROVs can also mount a cutter to enable them to cut the mooring of a moored mine.

ROVs are usually linked to the minehunter by way of an umbilical cable, which

PLATE 11.10   A *PAP 104* being lowered into the water. The suspended drag weight
is used to keep the vehicle at a constant height above the sea-bed. (*Photo: ECA*)

carries control information to the vehicle, and relays television and sonar data
back to the ship. To avoid the need for a heavy power cable, which would seriously impair mobility, vehicles generally carry their own power, either as batteries
or, in some cases, pneumatic. Typical endurance would be of the order of 30–60
minutes, after which the vehicle would have to return to the ship for recharging
and replenishment of expendable items, such as the mine disposal charges. To
avoid undue operational delays for this purpose, minehunters tend to be equipped
with two vehicles so that there should always be one available to be deployed.

There are many different types of ROV available these days. By far the most
widely used–almost 400 are currently in service around the world—is the *ECA
PAP 104*, shown in Plate 11.10. The latest version, the *Mk 5*, boasts all of the
features mentioned above.

NAVIGATION AND SHIP CONTROL REQUIREMENTS

Minehunting places fairly stringent demands on the control and navigation of a
vessel. During search, accurate control at slow speeds, along straight tracks, is
required. In good conditions, an experienced crew should be able to classify contacts without the vessel slowing down, but in less favourable circumstances, a

reduction in speed may be necessary, particularly if the density of mine-like objects is high or unknown. Identification and disposal, however, will take considerable time, and the vessel will need to be kept more or less stationary, or hovering, with respect to the contact, to allow an ROV or diver to be deployed, while maintaining good sonar contact with the target and remaining at a safe distance from it.

Accurate relocation of previously classified objects, and precise reporting of areas of coverage, are also important requirements. For this, positions of contacts must be determined and recorded at accuracies in the order of metres. This degree of accuracy must be attained in fixing the minehunter's datum position, the offset of the sonar towed body from it, and in the sonar's range and bearing measurement of the contact. Position-fixing requirements are discussed in detail in Chapter 12.

12

Route Survey, Navigation and Ship Control

In almost any naval operation there is a risk of enemy mining being encountered. An unambiguous means of disseminating accurately to friendly units details of known or suspected mining, and, just as important, areas known or believed to be clear of mining, is essential.

ROUTE DEFINITION

In NATO this dissemination is done through what is known as the 'Q Message' system, in which every route, area, channel and feature, on which reports of mining or mine clearance might need to be based, is allocated a unique identifying code, beginning with the letter Q. The second letter indicates the general geographical area, UK waters, for instance, using the letter Z, and a third letter the type of item—route or channel, for example. These three letters will be followed by a number to identify the item uniquely. A route somewhere around the UK might thus be given the code QZR123. It is this nomenclature which gives rise to the term 'Q Route', commonly used to refer to any predefined route for MCM purposes.

ROUTE SURVEY

In peacetime, operational planning should include the definition, maintenance and promulgation of details of Q Routes which are expected to be used in the event of a mining threat having to be prosecuted. These routes will be for the use of friendly shipping accessing naval installations and transiting between them, and should be chosen not only for the convenience of such shipping, but particularly for the ease with which the available MCM forces can provide the requisite level of confidence that they are clear of mining. To this end it is appropriate for the routes to be surveyed by MCM units well before operations begin in earnest. This is the process of Route Survey.

In preparation for possible defensive operations in one's own or other friendly waters, Route Survey can, of course, be conducted fairly thoroughly and comprehensively, but, as a prerequisite to offensive action in unfamiliar or enemy waters, some degree of compromise will almost certainly be necessary, taking into account the time and resources available and the threat to the MCM forces in carrying out the task.

ROUTE SURVEY DATA

From the point of view of the MCM organisation, route survey affords an ideal opportunity to gain familiarity with likely areas of operation, and, in particular, to acquire and maintain the vital and detailed knowledge of the environment and the minelike non-mines that will be encountered. Successive surveys of the same area will always yield some fresh information, either as a result of actual changes in the environment, or because of the inevitable discrepancies in records and measurements of different vessels, using different systems at different times, and so on. Assessing this new information, and updating the records accordingly, is a task which demands considerable experience and judgement. In view of the quantity of data involved, the task also lends itself in many ways to the application of current data processing techniques. The French Navy has had such a computer system in use for many years now, and it is managed by a team of experienced mine warfare officers and senior rates. In this regard, they are very much in the van of such innovation, with otherwise technologically advanced navies sadly lagging by a considerable margin.

To be useful, the mass of data collected and sifted by a route survey organisation must be made available to MCM units on task, as a Mine Warfare Pilot. This traditionally takes the form of a large book of printed data sheets, each depicting and describing one route or a segment of one. A typical example of this form of presentation is shown at Figure 12.1. Data reproduced in this form, however, are difficult, laborious and slow to maintain, and quite incompatible with the sophisticated data handling systems now fairly commonplace on MCM ships. To date there has been little progress in resolving this problem, and no standard for storing such data, or for transferring it between the computer systems which need it, has, as yet, been defined or agreed.

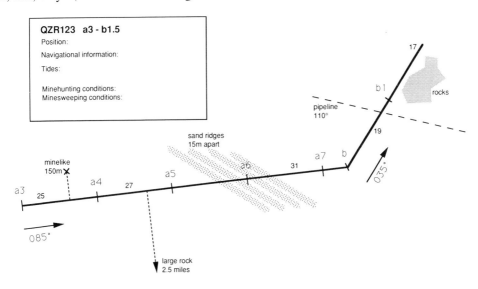

Fig. 12.1   Typical extract from a Mine Warfare Pilot, showing a segment of the route, significant underwater features, depths and general information about the area

Route Survey in Practice

Turning now to the route survey process itself, this can be performed by a conventional minehunter using its normal capabilities for search, classification and, possibly, identification to accumulate a comprehensive record of the area in question. Even though there may be no expectation of encountering mines, it will still be necessary, because of the way the minehunting system is designed to be used, to proceed fairly slowly if the search is to be conducted at all thoroughly. Rather faster progress is possible using some form of sidescanning sonar whose video output is recorded in its entirety for subsequent analysis. There may still be some advantage in an operator scanning the sonar picture at the time, and noting any contact which appears to be of interest, much as he would in any other type of search. To use the earlier type of single beam sonar for sidescanning, it is necessary to train the beam at right angles to the direction of motion, and to provide additional beam processing so that the narrow strips of sea-bed ensonified by successive pings can be recorded together to provide a contiguous picture. Such a practice was illustrated in Figure 11.5. More modern sonars have separate transducer arrays for sidescan operation. The extent of the total sonar footprint will depend upon the vertical beamwidth, the depth of the sea-bed below the transducer, and, possibly, the effective range of the s onar. The ensonified swath will typically be several hundred metres in width, but will not include a narrow strip directly below the transducer. Another, forward looking array could be used to cover this strip, but, in any case, it is likely that at least two parallel runs will be needed to achieve the full coverage required.

ROUTE SURVEILLANCE

When mines are suspected or known to have been laid along a route already surveyed, repeating the survey should readily confirm their existence and positions, since they should be immediately evident from a comparison of the two survey records. Searching along routes in this way in order to determine whether or not mining has occurred is known as Route Surveillance. Suitable machines exist to facilitate the comparison of sidescan sonar records; if conventional forward scanning sonar is used, the comparison will effectively take place on the sonar display at the time, when minelike contacts not previously recorded are detected. As there would, by definition, be a risk of encountering mines during route surveillance, it would be a wise precaution to use a forward looking sonar, if it is available, to give warning of anything directly in the path of the vessel.

Although route surveillance is likely to be carried out in the face of the threat of mines, and many of the specialised and expensive features of a minehunting vessel will be important to the effectiveness and safety of such an operation, route survey, by and large, is not. Mention has already been made in an earlier chapter of the COOP concept, and there is a large range of simple route survey systems becoming available for use on almost any type of platform. These systems typically comprise a commercially available sidescan sonar, with the transducers contained in a 'towfish', a suitable recorder for the sonar data, and an accurate navigation system. An example of such a route survey system is shown in Plate 12.1.

NAVIGATIONAL ACCURACY REQUIREMENTS

For most general operational purposes, navigational accuracies of the order of hundreds of metres are quite adequate, and most warships and other vessels are equipped accordingly. If, however, they are to take advantage of efforts to clear their intended path of mines, they must know exactly where the cleared path is, and follow it within the limits of its clearance. To allow for their own navigational inaccuracy, and the distance to which their influence on any remaining mines might extend, or at which such mines might still cause damage, a cleared path-width of 1000 metres or more is often required; this may well take several runs over parallel tracks by the MCM vessel. Any inaccuracy on the part of the MCM vessel in executing this task will require a corresponding reduction in the separation between these parallel tracks, and consequently more tracks will need to be run if gaps, or holidays, in the overall coverage are not to be left. This principle is illustrated in Figure 12.2. Fundamental requirements for an MCM platform, therefore, are to know its own position, and to follow a given straight track (over the ground), in both cases to a very high degree of accuracy.

The navigational accuracy requirement is also relevant to MCM operations themselves, for it is necessary for a vessel to be able relate previously recorded MCM data to the current task quickly and easily, mainly by way of positional correlation. In particular, there is a need to be able to return to deal with a mine or other suspect object, which may have been discovered quite a long time ago, possibly by a different platform. There has, in the past, been some debate as to whether these needs are better served by achieving repeatability, ie always measuring the same coordinates at a point even if they are not absolutely correct, or by actually achieving absolute accuracy every time. Even if all units were equipped with identical navigation systems, however, the natural variations in

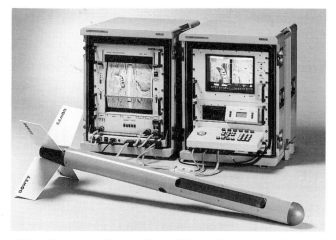

PLATE 12.1   The *Dowty Sidescan Sonar 3010*, for Route Surveillance and Mine Detection. (*Photo: DMOS*)

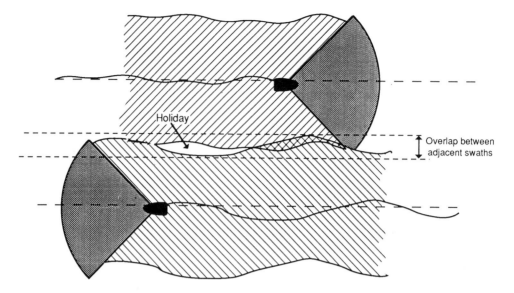

Fig. 12.2   The greater the navigational inaccuracies, the closer together must be
the parallel tracks, if holidays (gaps in the coverage) are to be avoided. In this
example, the tracks are too far apart and a small holiday has been left

conditions and equipment performance, and the uncertainties of availability
inherent in any likely operational scenario, render repeatability as such an imprac-
tical proposition. Repeatability is, however, implicitly achieved by aiming for a
high degree of absolute accuracy, and this has been considerably facilitated by the
advent of precise satellite navigation systems. Absolute accuracy is therefore the
goal.

Navigation Systems

To achieve absolute accuracy in a navigation system requires some form of fixed
ground reference, to which measurements taken on a mobile platform can be
related in order to determine the platform's absolute position. The most common
of these systems use radio signals from a number of fixed ground stations or orbit-
ting satellites. Alternatives include acoustic transponders on the sea-bed, bottom
contour profile matching, and tracking fixed targets, such as buoys, using the surveillance radar.

In systems which rely on a network of fixed points, the individual measurements
are generally single dimensional, such as the range from the point, and so at least
two will be needed to derive a position fix. In more general terms, each measurement gives rise to a Line of Position (LOP), which is the locus of all positions at
which that measurement could have been taken. Two such LOPs, then, which are
not too close to being parallel, are sufficient to give a position fix, but any errors
in either will not be immediately apparent. Using more than two is likely to show
up any inconsistencies amongst them, since they will not, in practice, all cross at a
single point, but it then becomes necessary to find the position which is the 'best

fit' to all the available LOPs. This concept is illustrated in Figure 12.3. Standard statistical techniques are readily applicable to this situation, provided that each LOP can be given a suitable weighting. The result will be the best position estimate derived from the available data, together with an error ellipse, which indicates the area within which the actual position is most likely to lie. Clearly the smaller the ellipse, the more certain the position estimate. Selecting the best LOPs to use when there are a number available, possibly from different systems, can be a tricky matter; assistance is provided on some of the more sophisticated equipments in the form of a graphical display of the LOPs from which the relevant geometry and the inconsistencies can be assessed.

Radio Navigation Systems

Radio navigation systems are of two main types. Some rely on essentially continuous transmissions from the fixed ground stations, which the receiver on the mobile platform takes in pairs, comparing them to derive their phase difference. The phase difference is a measure of the difference in the distances of the receiver from the corresponding transmitters, and so will give rise to a hyperbolic LOP. In practice these phase differences are actually angles, between 0 and 360 degrees, and so there will be a whole series of hyperbolic LOPs where that particular angle would have been measured, as shown in Figure 12.4. On the baseline, the imaginary straight line joining the two transmitter positions, these LOPs will be exactly half a wavelength apart, and it is normal to refer to the area between adjacent lines of zero phase difference as lanes, or sometimes zones. For practical purposes it is necessary to have some initial, albeit rough, position fix in order to resolve the lane ambiguity, before accurate position fixing is possible, although many more modern systems incorporate additional processing facilities to assist with this, including the use of coarser patterns of lanes derived internally from the received signals.

Probably the most widely used coastal radio navigation system is *Decca Navigator*. Indeed, many charts are overlaid with a lattice of *Decca Navigator* lanes to facilitate converting received data to actual position. There are a large number of chains of transmitting stations around many of the coasts of the world, each chain comprising a master and two or three slave stations. The receiver compares the phases of each slave signal with that of the master, and this results in hyperbolic LOPs for each slave. Various multiples of the frequencies actually received are used to give both coarse and fine patterns for each slave, and the fine lanes are of the order of 500–1000 metres in width (on the baseline). This gives an indication of the accuracy likely to be achieved, which, at best, will be about 25 metres, but in poor conditions and some way off the baseline where the lanes are several times wider, can be as poor as 500 metres or worse.

Although it is fitted to many vessels, the accuracy of *Decca Navigator* renders it of limited value for MCM purposes. A rather more accurate system is *Hyperfix*, developed from its successful predecessor *Hifix 6*. This system uses transmitting chains of three or more stations, and operates on a much higher frequency than *Decca Navigator*, giving lanes of about 70 metres baseline width. The signals can be paired in any configuration, so providing greater flexibility. Accuracy is of the

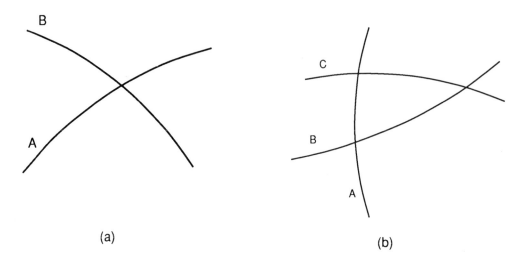

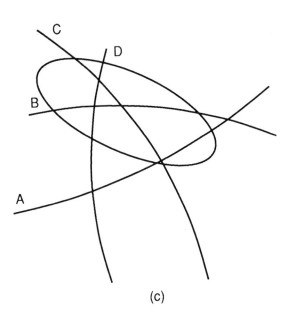

FIG. 12.3   With only two LOPs, as in (a), there is a unique solution where the lines cross. With more than two, there will not, in general, be a single point, as in the 'cocked hat' at (b). With sufficient LOPs, a poor fit by one of them—LOP A in (c)—is clear. In this third case, the error ellipse for the position estimate is also shown

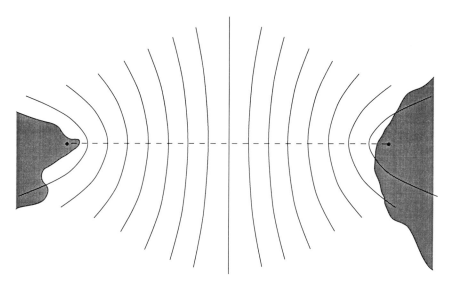

FIG. 12.4   The pattern of hyperbolic lanes for a pair of fixed transmitting stations
of a typical radio navigation system

order of metres, but, as with all hyperbolic systems, tails off with increasing range
from the transmitters.

The other type of radio navigation system operates at much higher frequencies,
and provides range measurements from each ground station, derived from the
time of propagation between transmitter and receiver. In some of these systems
the mobile station is active, that is it transmits a signal which is subsequently
returned by fixed transponders at the ground stations. The range can then easily
be calculated from the time difference between transmission and reception, allowing for propagation delays inherent in the equipment. Because the ground stations
need to respond to the mobile, there will be limitations in the number of
mobile stations that can be serviced by any given chain of shore stations. The other
approach is to use a passive mobile station, with a suitable time reference to
permit the necessary propagation times to be determined. In both cases, the
ranges can be used to define circular LOPs, but without the ambiguities inherent
in the hyperbolic systems described above. Accuracy is usually of the order of
a few metres, but operation is generally limited to within the lines of sight of
the ground stations, which, in practice, means rather less than 80 km. Typical
examples of this type of system are *Trisponder*, *Miniranger* and *Microfix*, which
use active mobile stations operating at microwave frequencies to give ranges
directly, and *Syledis*, in which a passive mobile receiver, operating in the UHF
band, provides range measurements which are actually pseudo-ranges.

The positions of the shore stations need to be known very accurately in order
to calculate the position of the mobile station. For *Decca Navigator* and many of
the *Hifix* and *Hyperfix* chains, the transmitters are fairly substantial installations
at fixed sites, and their positions, together with frequencies and other essential
parameters, are available in various publications. In most of the range-range

systems, the shore stations are easily portable, which is a major advantage when operating in a new area. If absolute accuracy is to be achieved in these circumstances, however, the positions of the stations will need to be surveyed precisely.

As has been indicated, good accuracies can be obtained with radio navigation systems, but there are certainG practical difficulties and limitations. The accuracy of hyperbolic systems varies with many factors, including distance from the transmitters and the pattern geometry, as well as the vagaries of radio propagation, which depend upon time of day, time of year, weather, and so on. The higher frequency range-range systems, on the other hand, are not prone to these problems, but are limited to line of sight, and can suffer from other types of propagation problem, particularly multi-path or reflection difficulties. One of the main operational drawbacks of all these systems, however, is their dependence on shore-based transmitters, which are vulnerable to enemy action or sabotage, either physical or electronic, and may not even be available at all in hostile areas. There is a need, therefore, for alternatives.

There are many other radio navigation systems available, but they all follow the same principles as those described above. Some of the mobile units from these systems are shown in Plates 12.2–12.5.

Satellite Navigation Systems

One alternative, now in widespread use, is satellite navigation, and specifically the *American Navstar Global Positioning System* (GPS). This comprises a constellation of 24 orbiting satellites, of which, at any point on the earth, there will always be at least four which are visible to a mobile receiver. The receiver determines ranges from the times of transmission of signals from a number of satellites, and then calculates its position, in two dimensions if only three satellites have

PLATE 12.2   The new *MK53 Decca Navigator*, which replaces the familiar *MK21* with its three dials (decometers) giving lane readings. The *MK53* gives a direct latitude and longitude read-out. (*Photo: Racal*)

PLATE 12.3 The *Hyper-fix Positioning System*. The central receiver/controller unit is needed for normal hyperbolic position measurement. With the other units, the transmitter and antenna tuning unit, range-range operation is possible.
(*Photo: Racal*)

been used, but in three dimensions if four or more have. There are two levels of accuracy available—the Standard Positioning Service with a specified accuracy of 100 metres and freely available to any user, and the Precise Positioning Service, with a specified accuracy of 18 metres, and available only to authorised users who have been supplied with the necessary codes.

The accuracy actually achieved from Navstar GPS or, indeed, any radio navigation system, can be enhanced by means of the so-called differential technique. This requires a second, fixed receiver located in the area of operation, and whose position is known precisely. This receiver determines the errors in the received information by comparison with its own, known position, and then transmits the error data to the mobile station over a suitable data link. Clearly this requires a considerable amount of additional equipment, and will be vulnerable to some of the problems of land-based radio systems mentioned earlier, but it can result in a dramatic improvement in accuracy.

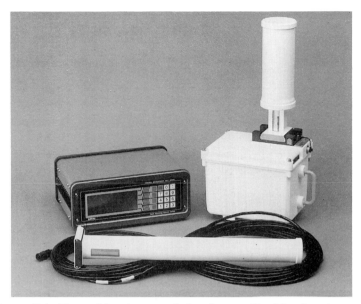

PLATE 12.4 The mobile elements of Racal's portable *Microfix* microwave position-fixing system, which can easily be fitted to a platform as and when required. (*Photo: Racal*)

PLATE 12.5 The *Syledis STR4* by Sercel. This system operates in the UHF band, and can work in Range-Range, Pseudo-Range or Combined Modes. (*Photo: Sercel*)

Other Types of Navigation System

There are also systems which do not rely on radio signals at all. A pattern of fixed acoustic transponders or transmitters on the sea-bed, for instance, can be used with suitable on-board equipment. Providing power for the sea-bed units for any length of time is difficult, and to achieve adequate accuracy requires a reasonably high frequency, which, in turn, limits the effective range, but such a system can nonetheless be of value in a small area, and when it is not desirable or possible to rely on a land based system.

A rather older technique, used before radio navigation systems became available, and still in use on some classes of ship, is that of tracking fixed targets with the navigation radar. The targets may be on shore, but these can prove difficult as radar targets. Special buoys, with a scope, or range of movement, of only a few metres are an alternative, and have the advantage of forming a self-contained system, in that they can be laid and recovered by MCM vessels, albeit with some difficulty, for their own use as and when required. The main disadvantage, however, is the inherent inaccuracies of the radar, which increase with range, and, even at short range, are excessive for MCM purposes.

Mention should be made of the use of the log and compass on an MCM vessel. It is possible to use these for dead reckoning, as on any ship, but this will not provide anything like the accuracy needed for MCM operations. In particular, a conventional, single-axis EM log will measure speed through the water only in the direction of the ship's heading, which may be rather different from the direction in which the vessel is actually moving through the water, especially when manoeuvring at slow speed. A twin-axis device will give more reliable measurements of velocity, but most MCM vessels now use one of the many types of doppler log available. These can measure velocity over the ground as well as through the water, and with somewhat greater accuracy than an EM log.

SHIP CONTROL

The ship control, or position keeping, requirement falls into two main areas—track-keeping and hovering. In both hunting and sweeping operations the vessel must keep as accurately as possible to a straight track (over the sea-bed) if uniform coverage of the area is to be achieved with the minimum of effort. When minehunting it is often necessary to maintain a fixed station, or hover, with respect to an underwater object during investigation and disposal. There is also a need for some form of position control in order to maintain station when team sweeping, and, during the early stages of development of the requirements for the Royal Navy's *Sandown* class, consideration was given to a facility for automatic control of circling around a contact at a constant range, but this was not eventually implemented.

Before the advent of computers on MCM vessels, position keeping had to be achieved by the helmsman with whatever limited navigational assistance was available to him. Some early navigation systems did provide a track guidance facility, which showed the distance of the vessel from a specified track or point. The first instance of any form of automatic control was on the *Hunt* class, which had a conventional autopilot, the set course of which could be changed dynamically under the control of the command system (*CAAIS*—see Chapter 13) according to an algorithm developed specially for this purpose. Despite the fact that this arrangement provides only indirect control of the rudders, in that the control algorithm in CAAIS regularly updates the course which the autopilot should steer, leaving the autopilot to control the rudders to achieve that course, it has proved remarkably effective in practice. No automatic control for hovering is provided, however, on the *Hunt* class.

For the *Sandown* class of Single Role Minehunters a more sophisticated approach was adopted, using a dedicated control system, interfaced to the command system, and with direct control over the *Voith Schneider* propellers and bow thrusters. The system allows fully automatic track-keeping and hovering, according to a predefined route or set of waypoints entered from the command system, as well as manual control by a joystick, which is very useful for close manoeuvres under bridge control. A somewhat innovative control principle was used to meet the hovering requirement, known as PCM, or Position Control by Manoeuvre, which differs from conventional DP, or Dynamic Positioning, systems, in that the algorithms are designed to maintain the ship's position by means of continual small manoeuvres, rather than by trying to keep the ship exactly stationary.

There are similar systems in use on almost all modern MCM vessels.

13
Command and Control

In this chapter the various aspects of MCM are brought together by considering the business of command and control, both on individual vessels and of a number of vessels when operating together to achieve a given objective.

MCMV COMMAND SYSTEMS

With the complexity and sophistication of modern MCMV weapon systems, and the huge quantities of data which must be processed, it is clear that, as is the case on other warships, a command and control system is needed. The basic requirements of such a system are to be able to store, manipulate and present to the operator the whole range of environmental, route survey and sonar contact information, to coordinate and, if necessary, process navigational sensor data to ensure that positional information meets the very high accuracy needed, and to pass the relevant outputs to a ship control system to enable precise manoeuvring of the vessel. There will also be subsidiary requirements such as data recording, analysis, training and so on, and possibly also more general functions to do with any non-MCM facilities of the weapon system, depending upon the needs and policies of the navy concerned. As far as information handling is concerned, it is also highly desirable that the information can be easily exchanged with other vessels' or shore-based data management systems.

Before the advent of computer systems on MCM vessels, a mechanical plotting table was used, with a rolling plot linked to the ship's log and gyro, and marked in chinagraph by an operator with sonar contact information as it became available. At this time there were no precision navigation systems in general use, and so there were considerable limitations to the effectiveness of this arrangement. The first example of a purpose built computer system being used was on the Royal Navy's *Hunt* class, for which a variant of the Ferranti *CAAIS* system, already in use on many of the Royal Navy's ships, was specially developed. It was accepted into service on the first of the class, HMS *Brecon*, in 1980. Although in many ways a great success, it was soon apparent that the fundamental differences in the command system requirements of MCM ships and conventional warships, and particularly the completely different data handling needed, had not been taken properly into account in specifying the system. These initial drawbacks were resolved by a substantial modification programme, resulting in an upgraded system, with vastly increased data capacity and a number of other enhancements. This improved system is now fully operational, and has proved very effective in service in the Gulf War.

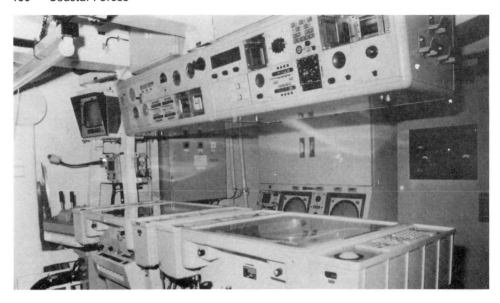

PLATE 13.1   The Operations room in HMS *Brecon* showing the Marconi *193M* console (background) and the two horizontal CAAIS displays used by the Minehunting Director on the left, and the Operations Officer. (*Photo: Ferranti*)

PLATE 13.2   The Operations room in HMS *Sandown*, showing the two dual display *2093* consoles and the two *NAUTIS-M* consoles. The Minehunting Director sits at his *NAUTIS* console, between the two sonar operators. (*Photo: VT*)

The Royal Navy's next generation of MCM command system was the Plessey, now Marconi, *NAUTIS-M*, which comprises three essentially identical consoles on a databus, each having its own processing and database. This system was designed specifically for the *Sandown* class, on which it is now operational, and is also being fitted to the US Navy *Avenger* class to supplement the existing *PINS* system, which lacks many of the display and data processing facilities necessary for an effective MCM command system. Although offering much the same functionality as the *CAAIS* system, it also includes some assistance with task planning, and takes advantage of more up to date technology for the displays, operator interface and the distributed database.

The arrangement of the main consoles in the operations room of the *Sandown* class is shown in Plate 13.2, where it can be seen that there are two *Sonar 2093* consoles and two *NAUTIS* consoles. The Royal Navy's standard minehunting watch comprises two sonar operators, one for search and one for classification, and two command system operators, the Minehunting Director (MHD) and the Operations Officer. The MHD controls the detailed minehunting process, and, in particular, the sonar and ROV operations. His console on the *Sandown* class is therefore in between the two sonar consoles. The Operations Officer takes a wider view of the task, and looks after the control of the ship's motion and position.

While the Royal Navy has tended to rely upon separate sonar and command systems, other navies have sought to combine them, an example being the French *IBIS* systems, produced by Thomson CSF. In these, the sonar picture and the synthetic picture used for command functions can be overlaid on the same screen, much as is the practice with radar pictures in many systems. Another example is the *Atlas MWS 80*, (Plate 13.5) used by the German Navy and also by the Royal Australian Navy on their *Rushcutter* class catamarans. In all these cases, fewer operators are needed, but they clearly must have a greater range of skills than is the case on Royal Navy vessels with separate systems.

HIGHER LEVEL COMMAND

Up until now, the emphasis has been on individual MCM platforms and their various diverse modes of operation. As a general rule, however, they do not operate in isolation, but must play their part in some grander scheme. For route survey, which, as has already been described, can be and often is carried out by single vessels on an opportunity basis, some higher level organisation is needed to coordinate activities and manage the vast quantities of data involved, and will also be responsible for determining routes to suit likely or defined operational needs. Mine clearance, on the other hand, will be much more directly associated with a specific operation, and will almost certainly have a number of vessels dedicated to the task.

It is worth recalling certain essential characteristics of MCM operations which largely determine the way MCM units must be organised and deployed. The most significant feature is the high degree of uncertainty which pervades almost every aspect of MCM, including navigational accuracy, the probabilities of detecting and correctly classifying a mine, and, in the event that no mines are found, the possibility that there never were any mines there in the first place. There are also many

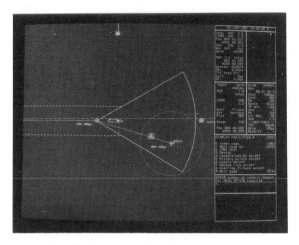

PLATE 13.3   A typical display presentation on the new colour version of *NAUTIS*.
(*Photo: Marconi*)

PLATE 13.4   The Combat Information Centre on the Swedish '*Landsort*' MCMV,
showing the single horizontal display console. (*Photo: Karlskrona Varvet*)

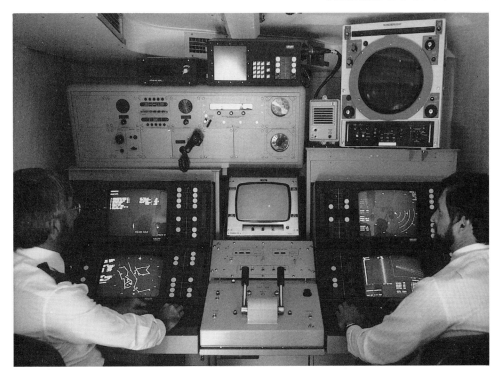

PLATE 13.5   A close-up of the *MWS 80*, showing the two command and sonar display consoles, with the ROV control panel between them. (*Photo: Atlas*)

different MCM techniques and systems available, and the choice of which to use will depend upon many factors such as the environment, the type of mine expected, the time available and so on. Furthermore, most MCM activities are both time consuming and very demanding of the crews involved; individual units must have time off task if they are to maintain their full effectiveness for any reasonable length of time. There is a clear requirement, therefore, for careful planning of the detailed tasks for MCM units, and for monitoring and assessing their achievements in order to remove, or, at least, reduce, the uncertainty inherent in the results.

The operational commander, faced with a mine threat, is interested in knowing, and reducing to an acceptable level, the risk to his ships and his objective. An MCM commander can therefore expect to be called upon to deploy his own resources to meet some specified goal in terms of the residual risk to shipping, and he will need to achieve a high level of confidence that he has actually met this goal. This, then, will be the essence of his task, and from this, and his existing knowledge of the routes and their environment, and of the capabilities of the MCM assets at his disposal, he must formulate a plan to achieve the goal in the time available. The units themselves must then be individually tasked and their progress monitored, in order that the MCM commander can assess what is actually being achieved, how this differs from what he planned, and any changes to his plan needed in consequence.

The task handed down to an individual vessel must include details of the area to be covered, probably, but not always, in terms of a specified length of a Q route and a channel width, the required degree of confidence or probability that no mines remain in that area, instructions on disposal of any mines that may be found, and any further information over and above that which will be obtained from the relevant Mine Warfare Pilot or equivalent. In specifying the area to be covered and the probability of clearance to be achieved, the MCM commander will need to be mindful of the likely effectiveness of the vessel's weapon system in the prevailing conditions, of the navigational accuracies likely to be achieved, both by the MCM vessel and by the ships which will eventually use the area, and of the degree of risk to those ships from the type of mine expected to be found. There are, of course, various formulae used by different navies in support of this task planning process, but there is little agreement as to which is the most appropriate in any given situation, and it can be assumed that there is no one way which is absolutely correct.

As individual units complete their respective tasks, the MCM commander must assess their results, both to measure progress towards his own objective, and to evaluate the probability of mines remaining in the area covered. He may then need to adjust the subsequent tasking in the light of this assessment. The results may also lead to an update to the local Mine Warfare Pilot information, and an assessment of the comparative effectiveness of each platform; this latter may reveal deficiencies or inaccuracies in individual sensor and navigation systems, additional training needs, and so on.

To carry out these functions, the MCM commander and his staff will need certain facilities and support. These should really include some form of computer system to perform the necessary calculations and analysis, and to maintain the large database of route and environmental data. Despite this fairly self-evident requirement, however, this is an area which has received comparatively little attention. Procedures and formulae used, and the exploitation of available data processing technology to automate them, have, with one or two exceptions, lagged well behind developments in many of the platform systems they are intended to support. The Royal Navy is currently in the very much protracted process, even by normal defence procurement standards, of developing a Mine Warfare Tactical Support System (MTSS), after abandoning earlier and rather more grandiose plans for a Computer Facility for Mine Warfare (COFAM). MTSS will be a small, transportable system for use by both MCM Tasking Authorities, in the manner described above, and higher levels of command. The French Navy, however, has been using a computer system for many years now to manage its route survey information, and probably still leads the field in this area. The Royal Australian Navy is endeavouring to establish a Mine Warfare Systems Centre, which seems to be intended to have rather more of the capability of the Royal Navy's aborted COFAM, in supporting low level tactical needs, for mining and MCM, analysis and evaluation of systems and their performance, development of mine warfare tactics, and so on.

To be really effective, the MCM commander needs a base somewhere in the vicinity of his area of operations, in order that he can quickly appreciate developments in the situation, and, when necessary, brief and debrief his subordinate commanders face to face. A portable cabin set up at a suitable shore site could be used, but he may sometimes have to operate from a platform at sea, although MCM vessels themselves do not, as a rule, offer sufficient space or facilities for this. The vessels will also need administrative and logistic support, since, unlike most warships, which are largely self-supporting for considerable periods, MCM vessels have an on-task endurance of only a few days and so require much closer support. This can be provided by a Forward Support Unit (FSU), which might comprise a number of transportable containers housing workshops, offices, stores, and accommodation for the support crew. The FSU would normally be established ashore, if possible, and could also afford the MCM commander and his staff a useful operating base. In the Gulf War, the Royal Navy's MCM force operated in this way, but with the containers set up on the RFA *Sir Galahad*.

14

Fast Patrol Boat Operations: An Introduction

A frigate or a cruiser has long since ceased to be a scout or a vessel 'in the van'. An aviation cruiser, as the Soviet Navy used to call its *Kiev*-Class ships, is not an aircraft carrier, even if this is to circumvent the restrictions on the passage of such warships through the Bosphorus. And drawing a distinction between destroyers and frigates is a hard nut to crack even for the expert.

These examples show that terminological inexactitudes in regard to the designations of warships are quite common and that a clear classification of ship types is not easy. An attempt to give a generally binding definition of any type of vessel is a problem that raised difficulties as early as 1919, when the Treaty of Versailles had to be interpreted. It is foreseeable that in arms control negotiations of the future, definitions will be a matter of hot debate. Moreover, there are linguistic subtleties and differentiations that are easily lost in translations or are simply untranslatable.

In consequence, 'fast patrol boat' (FPB), also cannot be a term providing an unequivocal description of a specific type of warship. The variety of units operated by the various navies under this designation is too wide for that. An exact definition of the vessel to be described is required.

Some Definitions

Generally, this naval weapon system is one of the big family of small fighting vessels, a classification largely governed by tonnage. The German term is *Schnellboot*, and the term used in this article is 'fast patrol boat' (FPB). The latter is used although, like the German one, it is inexact since it reflects only part of the characteristics required for the full operational spectrum of these craft. It is true that the German term *Schnellboot*—translated into English as fast patrol boat or sometimes even speed boat—characterizes an essential quality of such boats, but does little to show what they are required for. The English term, on the other hand, adds the patrol mission to the quality of speed. This means that the designation indicates an operating profile which, although it is indeed applicable, plays no more than a secondary role in the overall operational spectrum of the craft to be discussed in this chapter.

In this book we use the term FPB to cover small fighting vessels designed for missions in peripheral seas and offshore waters, armed with missiles and/or torpedoes plus guns and capable of running at high speed. This excludes from detailed discussion most of those vessels that are actually covered by the term 'patrol'. As we have already seen, patrol craft which are used for surveillance, policing functions, coastguard or border patrol tasks, fishery protection and many other missions lack the determinant characteristic which alone makes a vessel a FPB proper, i.e. speed.

This differentiation reduces the number of patrol craft, amounting to more than 5000 worldwide,[1] to about 1300[2] qualifying as FPBs. The latter figure which is still very high only accounts for vessels between 100 and 500 tons capable of attaining speeds of more than 30 knots and carrying the weaponry listed above. In English, these vessels are sometimes subsumed under the term 'fast attack craft' (FAC) and can be further broken down according to size, type of hull and armament. This results in precise designations such as 'fast gun boat' (FGB), 'fast missile boat' (FMB), 'fast gun hydrofoil' (FGH), 'fast missile corvette' (FMC).[3] Here, the term FPB is nonetheless used instead of FAC because the former is more commonly used in the NATO navies and is the usual designation found in the tactical publications of those navies.

Many shipbuilders have a long tradition in FBP construction. Besides the British shipyards of Vosper and Thorneycroft, now merged, the German *Lürssen Werft* is one of the leaders in the field of FBP construction. A continuous development can be traced from the initial vessels constructed by that shipbuilder during the First World War and having a displacement of 7 tons to the present-day 400-ton vessels of the *Gepard* class (*Type 143 A*).

Other typical representatives of the FPB type of ship were, in the Second World War, the British *Vosper 70* MTBs and *Fairmile D* boats and the German *S 100-Type* boats. Typical representatives are the British *Brave* and *Ferocity* classes, the German *Jaguar* and *Albatros* classes, the Danish *Willemoes* class and of course also the Soviet *Shershen*, *Osa* and *Matka* classes.

THE HISTORY OF THE FPB

The determinant factors which led to the development of FPBs were the invention of the torpedo—for many years the main armament of FPBs—and the use of internal combustion engines in naval shipbuilding, engines which were the first to enable comparatively small vessels to attain high speeds. But the years that mark the advent of these factors were far apart. The torpedo was developed as early as 1866, while internal combustion engines were not used in small warships until the end of the First World War. Therefore, developments did not converge for quite a long time.

The requirement for a mine to be precisely aimed at the enemy originated late in the 18th century soon after the discovery that it was possible to detonate gunpowder under water. Developing the mine had provided a weapon which could sink a ship if the explosive charge of the mine was adequate, a feat that the guns of the period as well as those of later epochs were not able to perform at all, or at any rate only with great difficulty.

It was the Austrian naval officer Luppius who succeeded in achieving the breakthrough. His invention was improved in 1866 by the Englishman Robert

PLATE 14.1   The Royal Norwegian Navy's *Stegg* is a 155-ton *Hauk* class FAC-M
or Fast Attack Craft-Missile, deriving its classification from its six *Penguin* Mk II
missiles. (*Photo: Royal Norwegian Navy*)

Whitehead who designed the first operational torpedo. Whitehead was also the
one who gave this weapon its name, the torpedo fish belonging to the family of
electric rays.

The mobile mine, now called the torpedo, could be aimed at the enemy and its
delivery had no longer to be paid for by the loss of the platform as with a 'ram
mine'. Its range of 200 metres was quite remarkable considering that in the Battle
of Lissa in 1866 the open-fire range was 920 metres.

The new weapon inevitably raised the question of a suitable delivery platform.
Carried as additional armament by large units, the torpedo was meant to be
the decisive weapon in a mêlée. In addition, its role was seen as that of the main
armament of smaller units which then were called torpedo boats. This concept
resulted from the realisation that a weapon was now available which allowed
large, heavy gun carriers to be sunk by smaller, actually inferior, units under
favourable conditions.

All the same, the torpedo boats that sprang into existence with the advent of
the new weapon cannot be seen unreservedly as the ancestors of FPBs. Their com-
monality lies in their main armament, the torpedo. Torpedo boats, however, had
not the superior speed which is a feature of FPBs.

FPBs, on the other hand, were not primarily used against large warships such
as battleships and cruisers. Seen against the background of what is known today

PLATE 14.2   *Puma* one of the German Navy's 391-ton *Gepard Type 143A* class of
FPB. (*Photo: F Lurssen Werft*)

it would have been reasonable later on to substitute internal combustion engines
for steam propulsion in torpedo boats and thus to arrive at the FPB type of
ship. But the development headed in another direction. The first torpedo boats,
some of them with a displacement of less than 50 tons, were found not to be sea-
worthy enough for operations in the open sea. Therefore, larger vessels were built
which soon arrived at displacements of between 100 and 200 tons. At the same
time, even larger units were constructed designed to control-one's own torpedo
boats as well as repel those of the enemy. For these units, initially called 'torpedo
catchers', 'torpedo hunters' or 'anti-torpedo boats' (contre–torpilleurs), the
term 'torpedo boat destroyer' was soon generally accepted. Since this type was
capable both of countering torpedo boats and of launching autonomous
attacks, and at the same time was largely oceangoing, it superseded small torpedo
boats in many navies. Thus the original anti-torpedo boat weapon system came to
develop into the multipurpose vessel for attack and defence, known as the
present-day destroyer.

The second factor stimulating the development of FPBs was the new opportunity to use internal combustion engines to attain speeds that had not previously
been attainable in small-ship construction. Since the beginning of the 20th century,
paraffin or petrol engines had been fitted in civilian vessels. In naval shipbuilding the use of such engines was initially confined to launches. It was not
until the First World War that navies called for small, fast craft for combat
missions.

The Imperial German Navy needed small, very fast vessels to remove British anti-submarine net defences off the Belgian coast. Since these were guarded by destroyers, the vessels designed to meet this requirement were fitted with a torpedo tube in addition to a machine gun. Because high-powered boat engines were not available, airship engines were used. And it was the airship engine (in German '*Luftschiffmotor*' (LM)) which provided the earliest name for the craft, '*LM-boats*'.

The Royal Navy considered a small, fast torpedo carrier a system capable of attacking the German High Seas Fleet which stayed most of the time in internal waters behind mine barriers and anti-submarine net defences. Such torpedo carriers were to be transported by large units to their area of operations where they were to be launched to make surprise attacks on the enemy who imagined that he was safe. The first vessels of this type were called 'coastal motor boats' (CMB) and carried one torpedo and one machine gun. Because of the non-availability of powerful boat engines, the British, too, used aero engines for them. For anti-submarine warfare also some fast boats were required and constructed.

The small vessels being constructed at the time, and whose displacement initially was about 10 tons, attained speeds of more than 30 knots, i.e. speeds unattainable with steam turbines in vessels of this size. Although the emerging units were used for many missions, the torpedo soon came to be the generally accepted main armament for them—with the exception of ASW units.

The small steam-propelled torpedo boats, also called 2nd class torpedo boats, which were used in many navies were not affected by this development. They were acknowledged naval weapon systems employed under proven operational concepts that provided for combined operations with heavy warships. Their replacement by the new FPB-type units was not in the offing. On the one hand, engine powers were not yet sufficient to permit steam engines to be replaced in boats, with a displacement of which was up to 100 tons; on the other hand, the war came to an end before the FPB had succeeded in establishing itself as a new naval weapon system.

As far as events in the First World War are concerned, therefore, the new type of warship merely played an inferior role yielding rather insignificant successes. Its most spectacular success may be seen in the sinking of the Austrian heavy combatant '*Szent Istvan*', 21,000 tons, by an Italian FPB.

Right to the end of the First World War, nobody recognized the operational capabilities that might be developed by continued improvement of the first FPBs. This applies in particular to the victorious powers. The smallest units mentioned in the Treaty of Versailles[4] were torpedo boats having a maximum displacement of 200 tons. Constructing FPBs of even remotely that size was ruled out by the limits to internal combustion engine development at the time. FPBs of more than 200 tons were not constructed until after the Second World War.

And yet it should be remembered that a new type of warship *had* been developed. To be sure, its true operational value still remained to be fully recognized, but the foundations had been laid on which to build further. From these early beginnings, a naval weapon system was created which then came to achieve notable successes and had an important share in fighting the Second World War.

The period between the two World Wars, although starting with a phase of

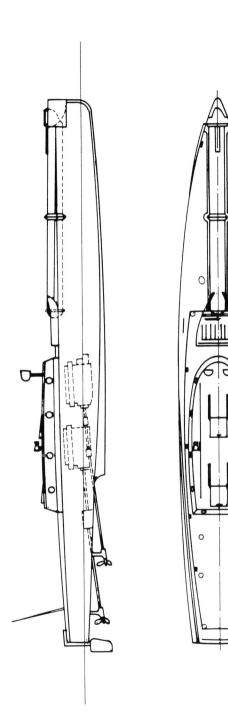

FIG. 14.1   The *LM Boot* of 1917 (*Lürssen Werft*)

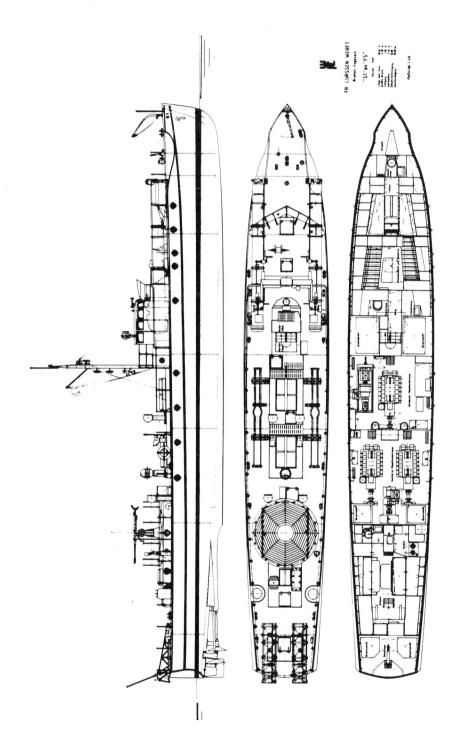

FIG. 14.2   The S-1 (Lürssen Werft)

stagnation in construction and development, was generally characterized by experiments with and trials of the new FPB naval weapon system. Tests were primarily concerned with naval architecture and propulsion.

The widest possible variety of hull forms and production methods were studied to find weapon platforms suitable for offshore waters. It is noteworthy that it was frequently the shipbuilders who imparted fresh impetus to these development efforts by constructing boats at their own expense and then trying to sell them to the navies.

Only a few navies, including the German and the Royal Navies, influenced FPB development actively, building up FPB fleets. Both navies had completed trials and were in possession of largely mature prototypes suitable for quantity production. The predominant type was fitted with two torpedoes as main armament and light automatic weapons for self-defence against units of equal size when running into them unexpectedly. Operations of FPBs against FPBs were not provided for in operational concepts.

Since 1931, Germany has used the designation '*Schnellboot*' for its FPBs. The British called theirs either 'motor gun boat' (MGB) or 'motor torpedo boat' (MTB), depending on their main armament, although both were carrying torpedoes. Besides, the British constructed 'motor anti-submarine boats' (MA/SB) for ASW operations. Their main armament instead of—sometimes in addition to—torpedoes was the only ASW weapon of the period: depth charges. The enemy boats were designated as 'E-boats' (enemy war motor boat).

Naturally, as soon as war broke out, an intensive development drive took place aimed at upgrading all kinds of weapon systems, including FPBs. The boats grew in size, their armament became more powerful and new technical equipment became operational. Additional defensive weapons were required to counter the new air threat. Radar development, too, was making rapid progress on the British side. It became possible to make the devices so small that they were part of the standard equipment of British FPBs by the end of the war.

PLATE 14.3   The German *S-1* torpedo-armed *Schnellboot* (*Photo: German Navy*)

After the Second World War, the sizable FPB inventory of the victors was reduced to peacetime strength, and the units of the defeated were divided among them. As after the First World War, a phase of stagnation followed. There were hardly any contracts for new constructions, so that the degree of improvement in existing designs was rather moderate for some years.

Then FPBs, constructed as improved versions of existing designs, again grew in size and were fitted with heavier armament. But their similarity to the wartime units, like that of other types of warship in the postwar period hits the eye. A decisive innovation arrived as late as about 1960 when the Soviet Union became the first nation to fit FPBs with missiles. This marked a new chapter in FPB construction, for the missile began to oust the torpedo from its role as main armament. The other nations followed suit and, by about 1975, most of the FPB navies had also fitted their boats with missiles. The present-day vessels of about 400 tons and with armament equivalent to that of a former light cruiser, however, represent a consistent development of the CMBs and LM-boats of the First World War era.

15

The Technology of FPB Operations

In this chapter the technological aspects of FPBs will be discussed: first of all the platform, but then principally armament and equipment. These factors will be considered in the perspective of the operational capabilities of FPBs. Generally, it will be the current technical configuration of modern FPBs which will be dealt with. In some fields a description of development will be given for better understanding, followed by a view of future capabilities. The discussion of weapon systems will address operational tactics that have an influence on the operational concepts which will be dealt with later on.

HULL FORMS AND CONSTRUCTION

Most present-day FPBs are either made of steel or composite built. In composite built hulls the internal structural members—frames, longitudinal and transverse girders—are made of light metal, while the skin and upper deck are made of wood. Both composite built and steel hulls are well-tested in FPB construction. Although steel is more easily workable and steel vessels permit more effective use of space, composite built vessels with their high strength and high flexibility are superior to steel built ones, especially in offshore waters. For reasons of economy, however, composite built vessels will virtually die out in the future in view of the fact that sheathing in tropical wood is very expensive. Instead, fibre-glass reinforced plastics and light metals will be used to a greater extent.

Since the very beginning of FPB construction, the ideal hull form has been a matter of dispute. The school of those who advocate the planing hull is about as strong as that of supporters of the classic displacement hull. Planing boats are faster with a given engine performance or attain the desired speed with less power. Displacement boats, on the other hand, have a markedly better seakeeping capability. Consequently, conceptual parameters—and among them primarily the intended area of operations—are the decisive factors in choosing the hull form. None the less, different parameters used by the Royal Navy and the German Navy in the last war resulted in the two hull forms being pitted against each other in one and the same area of operations. Most of the British boats were planing boats while the German Navy almost exclusively used displacement boats.

Hydrofoil craft, especially if fully foilborne, are superior in speed but have problems in confined waters and at low speed. The complicated foil control which

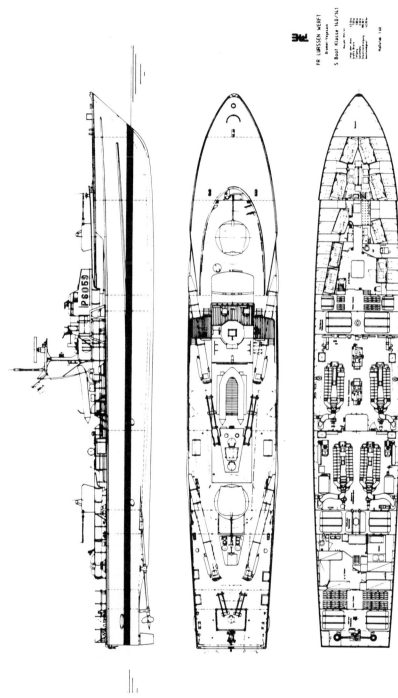

FIG. 15.1   The *Jaguar* class (*Lürssen Werft*)

PLATES 15.1, 15.2 & 15.3   Three photos which show the wooden construction
of the German Navy's *Jaguar* class FPB. These were built in the 1950s.
(*Photo: German Navy*)

ensures weapon platform stability in all sea states requires a very high tech-nological standard of the overall system, a requirement which in current designs still is a latent source of trouble or breakdown.[1] Air cushion craft, too, offer the advantage of high speed combined with the capability for amphibious operation. Their disadvantages are their relatively poor seakeeping capability and the very high engine power required. A broader use of these two types of craft is not fore-seeable because of the added disadvantage of extremely high building cost.

As to tonnage, conventional FPBs, both planing and displacement boats, increased steadily from below 10 tons in the First World War to more than 100 tons in the Second. Until the present, displacement has been continually increased. Today, FPBs displace up to more than 400 tons without having lost that designation. It is only larger vessels of between 500 and 700 tons such as the Soviet *Tarantul-* and *Nanuchka* class units which are designated as corvettes, although they would qualify as FPBs because of their construction characteristics and armament.

In spite of the FPBs' continual growth in size, the desired maximum speed of about 40 knots has been upheld, and this requirement is even met by displacement boats of 400 tons. While in the beginning, high-powered aero or airship engines were used, special ship's engines were developed later. Up to the Second World War the British almost exclusively used petrol engines. The Germans succeeded early in developing high-performance diesel engines, substituting them for petrol engines which were undesirable because of the attendant fire hazard. Since the increase in power of individual engines did not keep pace with the growth of the vessels in size while the speed requirement remained the same, an early transition was made from the two-shaft to the three-shaft vessel. Coupling of several engines by means of a gearbox was not realized because of the resulting high weight. Today, the FPBs of the German Navy usually are four-shaft vessels with one 4000 PS diesel engine per shaft. Owing to their small dimensions and higher power, gas turbines are more and more used in FPBs. They are characterised by savings in weight and space; however, the penalty of a markedly higher fuel consumption has had to be paid. So far, other types of propulsion, such as the hydrojet, have been incorporated in FPB designs in only a few instances.

TORPEDOES IN FPB

The classic FPB weapon was the torpedo. Two ejection tubes and two reserve torpedoes were the standard equipment of the Second World War boats. Postwar models were fitted with four tubes and seven torpedoes. While there was a wide variety of calibres well into the Second World War, a calibre of 53.3 cm was gen-erally accepted for the anti-surface torpedo worldwide after the end of that war; this was *inter alia* due to the dominating influence of US defence production. An explosive charge of about 300 kg and a total weight of 1.5 tons made this torpedo a weapon capable of destroying any warship. This lethal effect was however not achievable by an impact pistol but only by an influence pistol which detonated the weapon beneath the target. The resultant pressure surge lifted the target and inflicted structural damage which resulted in a total loss.

Until well into the 1960s, the greatest difficulty with the unguided, straight-running torpedoes of that generation was the solution of the fire control problem. In the Second World War the maximum torpedo range of 10,000 metres shrunk to operational ranges of 500 metres, since, in spite of a torpedo speed of 40 knots, the target had too much time to dodge an identified attack. Even if both target course and target speed remained constant, hits with unguided torpedoes fired at longer ranges were more or less accidental. If torpedoes had to be launched from unfavourable positions, the effective target width could shrink to the actual width of the target. And that target had to be hit by a weapon taking more than three minutes for its run when the range was two miles. Drift errors, irregularities in the straight run of the torpedo and influences of the medium, water, were apt to result in deviations that ruled out a hit. At a range of two miles, a one degree lead error resulted in a deviation from the desired point of impact of almost 70 metres.

Improvements were achieved by appropriate operational tactics, although at the expense of a high ammunition consumption. Any one target was attacked by several FPBs which fired their torpedoes simultaneously in spread salvos and from various aspects. Thus the torpedo runs covered possible evasive actions of the target.

Tests with torpedoes designed to run on preprogrammed courses in attacks against convoys or with torpedoes homing on sources of noise were emphatically called for. But until the end of the war such torpedoes never reached the stage of quantity production.

Wire-guided torpedoes, i.e. torpedoes controllable in terms of course, running depth and speed, however, achieved no more than a minimal improvement in hit rates, since current information on the torpedo's position at any given moment on its way towards the target was only obtainable by dead reckoning. Under water this method was inaccurate, and many of the familiar problems remained unresolved.

In the first post-war years, the wartime torpedo inventory continued to be relied upon. There was no advance in torpedo technology. From 1960 onwards, it was planned to substitute missiles for the torpedoes carried by surface units. This trend would also have spilled over to the FPB force (which actually wanted to stick to its torpedo armament) had it not been for the fact that development of more sophisticated versions of the torpedo for submarines, their only weapon, was a priority requirement. Thus, FPBs benefited from that development. The development objective was a torpedo that, in addition to being guidable, was capable of being influenced in other parameters as well. It was also to have a data feedback capability. As a result of that programme, the guidable torpedo, equipped with an active or passive homing head, became operational in Germany early in the 1970s.

Such torpedoes unreel a wire over which they can be guided and along which they in turn signal back sonar location data to the vessel launching them. This permits accurate target discrimination and evasion of the target's decoys. The guiding wire carries a two-way data link between weapon and platform. Course, speed and running depth are variable at any time. The torpedo sonar can be switched to the active or passive mode, and, even on its homing run, the torpedo's track can be corrected or directed onto a different target. The torpedo feeds back all parameters in true values, so that comprehensive information is available at the platform, enabling it immediately to react to any move of the enemy.

Unlike a missile, a modern torpedo cannot be intercepted. It no longer gives itself away through its wake of exhaust and the noise of its engines but is propelled to its target quietly by electric propulsion without leaving a wake. Since the target has no opportunity at all to detect a torpedo attack, it is incapable of active defence. Precautionary evasive action by the target, or the use of decoys, are identified by the torpedo gunner—or in autonomous homing by the homing programme—and are anticipated. If the guiding wire is cut early, a computer installed in the torpedo takes over control. The pre-programmed course guides it to the vicinity of the target, and the computer makes the sonar seek and, having obtained sonic bearings, makes it home accurately on the target. The firing vessel, for its part, also unreels a wire and can leave its firing position without imposing a tensile load on the guiding wire. Moreover, this technique reduces the period for which FPBs are tied down for tactical reasons. However, in spite of its modern configuration, the torpedo is being increasingly pushed into the background by missiles. This is essentially due to the longer period for which the firing FPB is tied down tactically and to the shorter range of torpedoes.

It has been realised just recently that, beset as the torpedo may be by the weaknesses mentioned above, it is a fact that unlike any other weapon, including missiles, it does not leave any real chance of defence to the enemy. In addition, the torpedo, in contrast to the common missile, has a lethal effect on a target. The reassessment of these two facts will probably ensure that the torpedo will continue to be a main armament of FPBs in addition to missiles for a long time to come.

FPB GUNS

The guns carried by FPBs have almost always been an additional or secondary armament; even the majority of all MGBs were armed with torpedoes, in spite of their name. Regardless of their differing roles, the guns carried by the various classes of FPB were largely identical. For the main criterion in regard to the numbers and calibres of guns carried was the size of the vessels concerned. In view of their heavy weight, their installation—on the forecastle, in particular, where the torpedo tubes were mounted—met with problems. Displacement boats had a definite advantage in this respect, for planing boats experience particular difficulties with additional weight on their forecastles. Originally, guns were carried as defensive weapons to counter equivalent enemy craft—a combat situation which was best avoided. For this purpose, machine guns and other light automatic weapons were considered sufficient. The heavy air threat in the Second World War made the fitting of additional small-bore anti-aircraft weapons a must. Furthermore the Second World War produced combat situations in which FPBs had to fight FPBs despite the old philosophy against such actions. This created a call for heavier guns. In consequence, the main calibre of FPBs' one or two rapid reload guns was increased to as much as 40 mm. In addition, there were several automatic guns of up to 20 mm. Although the designation MGB suggests heavier calibres, they, too, had guns of no more than 40 mm. While heavier calibres would have done more

PLATE 15.4   *Bussard* one of the German Navy's *Type 143* was built by Lurssen's in 1976 and carries four *Exocet* missiles, two 76 mm Oto-Melara guns and two 21"/533 mm torpedoes aft. (*Photo: German Navy*)

PLATE 15.5   The Royal Swedish Navy's 210-ton *Spica I* class FPB of the 1960s had the 21-inch torpedo as its main weapon. (*Photo: Royal Swedish Navy*)

damage, they were not practicable for reasons of weight. Moreover, engagement of highly mobile targets, FPBs and aircraft, required a high rate of fire if hits were to be scored. At the time, this was only achievable by the use of fairly light weapons.

Towards the end of the Second World War, some German FPBs were equipped with a 40 mm gun of Swedish origin. An improved version of that gun later became the standard weapon in Western navies. Having a rate of fire of 240 rounds per minute and a total weight of 2.6 tons, it met the essential requirements a weapon designed for small vessels was expected to fulfil: light weight and a high rate of fire in conjunction with a relatively large calibre.

PLATE 15.6   The 57 mm *L70 Mk 2* Bofors gun of the Royal Swedish Navy's *Spica II* class of Fast Attack Craft in action. (*Photo: Royal Swedish Navy*)

PLATE 15.7   *Iltis* one of the German Navy's *Tiger/Type 148* Class of FPB is armed with a 76mm OTO-Melara forward and a one 40mm Bofors gun aft. It was built by CM de Normandie of Cherbourg in 1972. (*Photo: German Navy*)

Until about 1960, all FPB guns without exception were laid optically, either directly from the gun or by separate target designators or directors. It was only later that radar fire control facilities were compact enough to permit FPBs being fitted with them as well. This resulted in a substantial increase in combat power, since the boats' guns now had an all-weather fighting capability.

Late in the 1960s, many NATO navies started introducing an Italian 76 mm gun as their new standard weapon. The development of this compact gun is noteworthy in particular because in spite of its calibre, its comparatively light weight of 7.5 tons makes it suitable for use in small vessels. Of course, the boats had meanwhile grown in size to more than 200 tons. This gun with its high rate of fire and preload capacity can be switched directly on to a fire control system and requires personnel for reload only. Firing newly developed ammunition, capable of being switched from anti-surface to anti-air operation, this gun meets all requirements to be expected from a weapon designed for small vessels.

With a few exceptions, such as the Norwegian *Storm* class boats fitted with a 76 mm anti-surface gun, the guns carried by FPBs are both anti-surface and anti-air capable. In spite of this increase in calibre, their suitability for anti-surface operations and good fire control equipment, guns have remained a secondary armament in FPBs. The principle is: FPBs are not gun boats. This means that in torpedo and missile carriers, guns are carried primarily for self-defence especially against the air threat. It is only in exceptional cases that guns are used against surface targets. First of all, this is due to the limited ammunition load which rules out anti-surface engagements, with their high ammunition consumption, in offshore waters where the air threat is generally heavy. Another reason is the high risk to the firing vessel in an exchange of gun fire, or dogfight, as it is called.

High-speed aircraft, and missiles even more, can only be engaged effectively during a straight-in approach or in their 'flat trajectory' phase, respectively. Lead calculation under other conditions or for crossing targets will result in errors that will no longer permit hits on such high-speed targets in spite of ammunition with great lethal radii. Missiles have to be hit at a range which ensures that the kinetic energy of their fragments cannot harm one's own vessel.

Guns carried for anti-missile defence are either relatively large-bore weapons (76 mm) firing expensive ammunition over long ranges or multibarrel guns of small calibres (from 20 to 30 mm). The effectiveness of these guns, designated as 'point defence weapon system' (PDWS) is due to their high rate of fire, rounds made of special alloys and an integrated fire control system providing accurate firing data without parallax errors.

As a rule, modern FPBs are equipped with two guns. The forward gun is a large-bore weapon, the aft gun in most cases a smaller bore weapon or PDWS.

In spite of the fact that missiles are coming to be more frequently used to fight air targets as well, a complete replacement of guns by missiles is not in the offing. This is for several reasons: anti-surface missiles have a 'minimum range' inside which they cannot be used. Without guns, a missile carrier is defenceless within this range, which may be as much as several miles, depending on the system. Moreover, guns are more responsive than anti-surface missiles which, depending on their technological standard, require anything up to several minutes to become operational. In surprise encounters, therefore, guns will be needed.

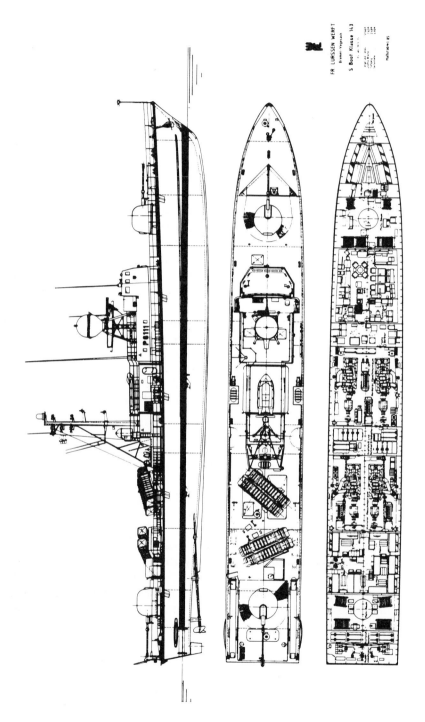

FIG. 15.2   The *S-143 class* (*Lürssen Werft*)

Targets keeping close in-shore and shore-based targets cannot be engaged by missiles and so also require the use of guns. Furthermore, the technological development of guns has not yet hit the ceiling of potential capabilities. 'Intelligent' or 'smart', e.g. terminally guided, ammunition will provide a substantial increase in the effectiveness of guns.

FPB MISSILES

Fitting FPBs with surface-to-surface missiles started in or about 1960 in the Soviet Union. For 10 years the USSR with its *Komar* and *Osa* class FPBs had a definite lead over the Western boats in the Baltic area. The missile nicknamed *Styx* by NATO had a range of 11 nautical miles. The target was acquired and tracked by its radar homing head. This made the missile the first 'fire and forget' SSM used in FPB-size units. This term means that once the SSM has been fired, the firing unit is no longer tied down for tactical reasons; on the other hand, the unit is no longer able to influence the SSM. The condition requisite for this technique is an accurate target position which is fed into the SSM before launch; in the vicinity of that position the SSM will, after a mid-course phase, use its radar homing head or other detection system to obtain exact target data for its terminal phase.

Nowadays SSMs are part of the standard equipment of modern FPBs. In the NATO navies the French *MM 38*, the US *Harpoon* and the Norwegian *Penguin* are those most commonly used. There are 4 to 8 of them per unit. *MM 38* distinguishes itself by a particularly low flight profile which makes it a 'sea skimmer'.

Warsaw Pact missiles have total weights of 2200 to 3000 kg[2] and warheads whose explosive power can be lethal for units up to destroyer size. Western missiles, such as Harpoon and MM 38, in contrast, have weights of about 700 kg[3] and proportionately smaller warheads. But the sought-after success of battle, viz. neutralising the enemy, so that he cannot continue his mission, can be achieved equally well by such missiles against units up to destroyer size, if just a single hit is scored.

The essential requirements to be fulfilled by modern missiles may be subsumed under the terms hit accuracy and high effectiveness. To meet these requirements, a missile must have many performance characteristics that, for technical reasons, cannot be combined in one single system. The various requirements for instance have conflicting effects on the dimensions of the missile. A SSM should be small in order to make its detection difficult and to permit the maximum possible quantity to be shipped. Its warhead should be powerful enough to have an adequate effect on target. Its range should be so long that the firing unit can stay out of the enemy's reach. Its flight altitude should be very low, making the missile difficult to locate and hence to engage. Its speed should preferably be in the supersonic range to minimise the chances of defence and to leave little time to the enemy to move away from his original position. The integrated radar should be activated as late as possible to leave the minimum possible time for electronic countermeasures. Its own radar should be insensitive to countermeasures. The radar search window should be reducible to so small an aperture that target discrimination is possible—in particular for targets keeping to the shore. The

PLATE 15.8   The Royal Norwegian *Penguin* was originally developed in the 1960s
and was the first anti-ship missile with infra-red homing. The *Mk III* has a range of
40km. (*Photo: Royal Norwegian Navy*)

PLATE 15.9   Like most FPBs, *Gnist* one of the Royal Norwegian Navy's *Storm*
class FPBs, carries no surface-to-air-missiles. (*Photo: Royal Norwegian Navy*)

radar seeker should be complemented by another homing system—IR or TV—to eliminate target errors through correlation of target information. The reaction time of the overall missile system should be short to permit the weapon to be launched immediately upon receipt of the target data. An additional requirement is optimal integration of the missile into the FPB weapon system to keep the over-all reaction time short.

In contrast to SSMs, surface-to-air missiles (SAM) are not yet part of the standard equipment of FPBs. Although the first Soviet missile corvettes (*Nanuchka*) carrying a SAM system were constructed as early as 1968, such systems were not fitted in series-produced small units with the exception of experimental types. Furthermore, they were primarily designed for anti-aircraft defence, and their suitability for anti-missile defence is limited, since the latter requires defence weapons of higher quality. Other SAM systems, both Western and Eastern, that would be qualified for anti-missile defence as well are still too heavy and complex, so that there are limits to their being fitted in FPBs unless one would install them at the expense of other weapons.

But the requirement for complementing FPB armament by a SAM system with an anti-missile capability is justified by the change in the threat to the boats. The threat has come to be primarily a pure missile threat posed by sea-based, airborne or land-based platforms that will no longer be within reach of FPB weapons.

SAMs that are to be used against missiles in the first place should meet the following requirements: extremely short reaction time both of the missile and of the weapon system, and supersonic speeds, since engagement is critically dependent on the time factor. A SAM-integrated active homing system or passive 'home on radiation' and 'home on IR' system is needed to permit interception of missiles of different designs. A SAM system to be used in FPBs should also be compact.

Except for variants of the '*Fliegerfaust*' there is as yet no operational SAM system suitable for small vessels. A US–German development, the 'rolling air frame missile system' (RAM) is nearing completion and will largely meet the requirements to be expected from a SAM system.

Under the aspect of sustainability of naval weapon systems, antimissile cap-ability is gaining central importance. To counter the threat posed by modern missiles, effective anti-ship missile defence (ASMD) requires co-operation of all systems available on board. Since ASMD is also very critically depending on the time factor, all measures taken must be co-ordinated by computer support and some of them must even be initiated by the computer automatically. ASMD on the one hand aims at a mechanical destruction of the missile through a 'hard kill' effected by gunfire or SAM. On the other hand, 'soft kill' action is to make the missile miss its target or to deflect it from a target already located and tracked. The 'soft kill' is effected by electronic countermeasures (ECM).

FPBs AND ECM

ECM include jammers that prevent the enemy missile radar from acquiring its target or deceive it by false echoes, so that it flies past its target. Chaff is another type of ECM. Clouds of chaff are generated to offer the missile false targets

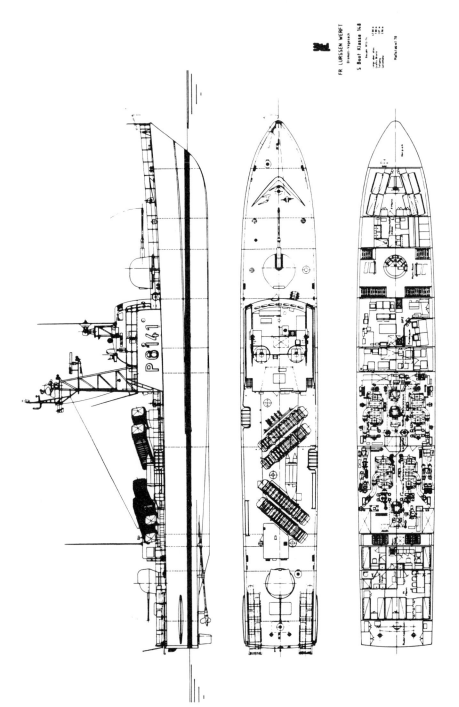

Fig. 15.3   The *S-148* class (*Lürssen Werft*)

complicating its task of target selection or to lure it away from the right target by the larger radar echoing area of the chaff cloud. To counter IR homing heads, ejectable heat generators are used whose effect resembles that of chaff.

The importance of ECM as a survivability factor is not confined to ASMD. ECM are just as important for the employment of one's own weapons. Chaff can not only irritate the missile homing head but can also obscure the situation to the enemy, complicating his target selection when he prepares his attack. The situation can also be obscured both through jamming the enemy's radar frequencies or electronic generation of false targets. In an environment of electronic jamming, the enemy, apart from his being prevented from using his own weapons, will no longer be able to defend himself, since attacks will not be identifiable. In addition, jamming of communication frequencies may be used to deny the enemy exchange of information between his units or to interrupt his links to his operational control centres. The goal of any ECM is to disrupt the enemy's command and control capability in order to prevent him from using his weapons effectively while one retaining one's own command and control capability and being able to employ one's weapons freely.

THE IMPORTANCE OF SPEED

The speed of FPBs is not merely the criterion which singles them out from the bulk of patrol boats; for many years speed has also been a must for weapon employment and for ensuring survivability. In the times before the advent of radar, FPB speed permitted swift penetration to torpedo range and a quick get-away out of the reach of enemy guns. It left the enemy but little time for defence. Although destroyers and frigates are capable of reaching comparable speeds, they need comparatively deep waters for reasons of fluid mechanics. In the shallow waters of offshore areas, therefore, they are clearly inferior to FPBs in terms of speed.

It is high speed combined with great agility which permits FPBs to dodge the enemy's gunfire at longer ranges. During the time of flight taken by the shells the FPB's course can be altered so much that he is no longer at the predicted point of impact. In blind firing, not all modern fire control systems are able to engage fast, zigzagging targets; rather, they must apply complicated firing procedures to try and cover prospective evasive action. Such methods are however very expensive in ammunition.

For modern FPBs the importance of speed has diminished, except under gunfire. This is due to detection systems ruling out surprise and undetected penetration, and to missiles for whose employment and interception speed plays a secondary part. Nowadays, the advantage high speed confers on FPBs is high mobility. Even from rear positions they can deploy swiftly to remote areas of operation where they can concentrate combat power by surprise. Intelligence reports can soon 'age' when FPBs redeploy to other waiting areas after having been identified. This makes it more difficult for the enemy to plan his space/time factors, for he must continuously expect to be attacked by FPBs during his own actions in confined waters.

PLATE 15.10 The Maybach diesels of the Royal Norwegian Navy's *Storm* class of FPB develop 7200 hp and an impressive turn of speed. (*Photo: Royal Norwegian Navy*)

SENSORS AND C³

The sensors and C³ facilities carried by modern FPBs are qualitatively equivalent to those found on board the considerably larger frigates and destroyers. For reasons of space and weight, most FPBs carry merely a combined surface and air surveillance radar. The requirements to be met by modern equipment are: long range combined with short give-away range; interlock circuits against jamming; track while scan.

Fire control radars which must be just as resistant to jamming serve the direction of guns and can be used as standby for surface surveillance. In view of the general susceptibility of radar equipment to jamming and detection, gun direction is also effected by optical, IR, laser and low light level TV (LLTV) equipment. It is not mandatory for each weapon to have its own sensor. Target data can also be collected by one sensor for several weapons simultaneously. The goal is, however, to have enough sensors to ensure a capability of employing all weapons at one and the same time.

For FPBs, passive sensors for electronic support measures (ESM) rank equal in importance with their active sensors, i.e. radar. These receivers detect and analyse the electronic emissions of the enemy. Emission analysis determines the type of the enemy radar emitter and hence that of the platform carrying it, and of the threat. In addition, a bearing is obtained which is correlated with those obtained by other units to locate the position of the detected enemy. Modern systems also use the results of this analysis for the control of the ECM system or, as the threat requires, for automated defence.

In addition to the classic communications facilities, primarily encrypted radio teletype and radio telephony, FPBs are now carrying an automatic data exchange system. In the mid-70s the German Navy fitted its FPBs with computerized command, control and information systems. This was the first time for *LINK 11*, the standardised data link system of NATO, to be installed in units of so small a size.

LINK 11 in combination with computerised C² and fire control systems was a milestone in the development and operational control of FPBs. Not only does this put them on a par with destroyers and other large combatants but it also enables them to co-operate with all forces equipped with *LINK 11*—from destroyers and frigates over helicopters to NATO *E3A AWACS*—within the integrated data system linking all of them with each other. Moreover, a data link with the MHQ can be established as a C² link.

CHARACTERISTICS AND ROLES

FPBs are used as minelayers, particularly for mine warfare in maritime areas exposed to an intensified threat. Their advantage lies in their speed which allows swift execution of minelaying operations, and in their strong armament which makes the protective units otherwise required for such operations superfluous. For reasons of weight and stability, their payload is relatively small, a disadvantage capable of being offset by the number of platforms. The 100-ton boats of the Second World War were capable of loading 6 mines, the contemporary 400 ton boats carry many times as much. The additional load, however, restricts the sea-keeping capability and maximum speed of the vessels.

Although in the Second World War FPBs, thanks to their shallow draft, ran unharmed over moored mines lying in wait for submarines and large units in deep minefields, they were and are of course exposed to a mine threat. The reaction times of pressure and acoustic firing mechanisms are so short that overrunning them at high speed does not ensure safety. Magnetic firing mechanisms are the ones against which some degree of protection is achievable through installation of self-protective systems.

Although FPBs are occasionally used as ASW vessels, this is not one of their typical roles. Obtaining good results from underwater detection equipment requires low self-noise, a characteristic that is not achievable in FPBs. High speed,

PLATE 15.11   The ships of the Royal Swedish Navy's *Spica II* class of FPB are often used for ASW purposes in coastal waters. (*Photo: Royal Swedish Navy*)

noisy diesel engines or gas turbines and up to four high-speed propellers are factors that strongly degrade underwater detection. All the same, there are methods, applied especially in the Soviet Union and in non-aligned Sweden, of using units which definitely qualify as FPBs for ASW operations. Similar to helicopters employed for ASW operations, these FPBs stop their engines for detection and then proceed to new positions where they continue their detection operations. As underwater weapons, ASW torpedoes and missiles are commonly used besides depth charges.

NATO navies have discontinued using FPBs for such operations. Hence ASW detection equipment and weapons are not required on board FPBs—not even for self-protection, since FPBs largely operate in areas whose shallow depths rule out the presence of submarines. Even in other waters, the submarine threat can largely be neglected since FPBs are not assumed to be 'primary targets' of submarines and since their high speed and rapidly altering courses make it practically impossible for submarines to solve the fire control problem.

16

Operational Concepts: FPB in the Second World War

Accounts of FPB operations of the First World War do not indicate what, if any, operational concepts existed at the time. The operations varied too much. They ought to be seen as those of a new naval weapon system in its experimental stage rather than as operations reflecting any particular concept. However, the initial FPB missions do indicate a versatility of this type of craft which has been confirmed in the course of the subsequent history of its development. First World War FPBs were mainly employed as fast torpedo carriers, pitted against big surface units; besides, there were a number of other roles such as minelaying, commando operations, coastguard and escort missions, reconnaissance and ASW operations.[1]

From among the capabilities which had been demonstrated in the First World War operations, the British selected two very different ones before the Second World War for which they developed operational concepts: torpedo delivery and ASW operations. MASBs, true to their name, were to operate against enemy submarines in the coastal zone. In the Second World War, however, this concept did not prove a success, since German submarines mostly operated outside British offshore waters and hence beyond the limited range of MASBs.[2]

MTBs were constructed for the surveillance and defence of the coastal zone. Their prospective targets were destroyer-size surface units. The command authorities of the Royal Navy, like those of other blue-water navies, were not very interested in such small units.[3] Nevertheless, the fact that upon the outbreak of the Second World War Great Britain had five FPB flotillas and was able to rely on experienced shipyards for further construction is *inter alia* a credit to the shipbuilders who constructed for export and tried over and over again to attract the Admiralty's interest to the new designs.

The nature of the FPB construction activities, starting upon the outbreak of war, was that of reaction to a course of action by the enemy which had not been foreseen. On the one hand, German FPB attacks against coastal shipping off the British coast required many small, fast units for the protection of convoys. On the other, the German E-boat threat had to be countered by tactical offensive operations. Of the existing units, MTBs and MASBs were too qualified for this role and were made into FPB hunters by fitting them with additional guns, thus converting them to MGBs. Thereafter MGBs were constructed in large numbers as a specific match to E-boats. British MGBs operated in groups of four to six units[4] to achieve superiority in battle through concentration of combat power.

All British FPBs were deliberately designed as planing boats in order to attain superior speed. This was necessary from the British point of view to cut off the E-boats' withdrawal, to deploy to positions off gaps in the German mine barriers screening the operating bases along the occupied Channel coast, and to attack the returning FPBs from such positions.[5] For the purposes of that operational concept this decision was correct and stood the test of time. However, during the war it turned out that the Germans were particularly successful in marginal weather conditions as they were still able to go to sea in their displacement vessels without being molested by MGBs, since the British boats had to stay in their bases in such weather. As the British forces grew in strength, the success of the German FPBs was entirely contingent on marginal weather conditions.

The German Navy pursued FPB construction from 1926 onwards, at first secretly because of the provisions laid down in the Treaty of Versailles,[6] then officially and legitimately under the 1935 Anglo–German Agreement regarding the Limitation of Naval Armament. The goal of FPB construction was to provide a number of smaller torpedo-carrying FPBs in addition to the torpedo boats permitted under the Versailles Treaty. Operationally, however, they were to be employed like the First World War torpedo boats, i.e. in combination with major combatants against the enemy's large units.[7]

In 1934, however, the FPB mission was revised and defined as 'destruction of enemy major combatants and cruisers'.[8] This concept was based on the assumption that the French would impose a blockade on Germany. FPBs were to operate against blockade forces in the North Sea.[9]

The German Navy had not envisaged having the British as an enemy early enough to allow the conceptual and material preparations necessary to meet this threat to be completed by 1939. This unreadiness applied to all forms of warfighting at sea and not just to FPB operations. In spite of Great Britain being an additional opponent, the FPB mission was not revised until well into the war. The anticipated blockade did not materialise, owing to the change in the enemy situation, and hence the operational concept could not be brought to bear either. The occupation of France produced a new geostrategic situation for naval warfare, one which no longer called for FPB operations as originally envisaged. A stop to FPB construction was therefore considered[10] but not ordered.

In 1940, at last, the FPB mission was revised and adjusted to the new situation as follows: 'Operations against convoys off the British coast'.[11] The 'FPB commander' was free to decide whether to attack convoys directly or to take advantage of the minelaying capability of his units to accomplish his mission by mining the convoy routes.

German FPBs did not operate as lone hunters. The concept was to mount operations in flotilla strength comprising eight to ten boats. Owing to losses, however, the boats mostly operated in groups of three to four. Like the British, the Germans had to concentrate forces with the aim of establishing local superiority. Furthermore, some torpedo tactics required co-ordinated action of the boats. Laying of minefields, too, required several delivery platforms operating together to ensure the planned effect of the mined area.

Initially, the German FPBs were very successful in their torpedo and mining operations against British supply shipments, as reflected by the high tonnages

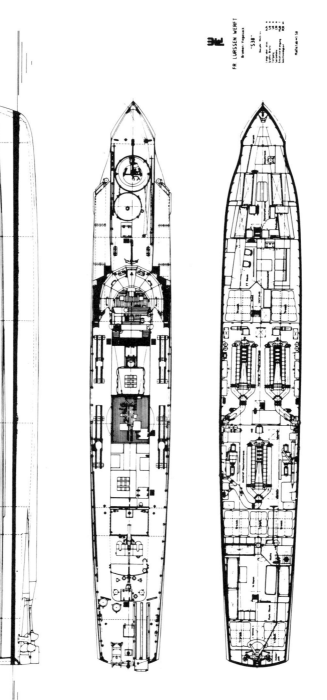

FIG. 16.1   The *S-38* (*Lurssen Werft*)

sunk in relation to the number of FPBs participating in such operations.[12] In the face of British air superiority, German FPBs only operated at night or in bad visibility. Although this prevented them from exploiting their radius of action in the short summer nights, it enabled them not only to evade the direct air threat but also to deprive the enemy of early warning by aerial scouts. Because of the shorebased listening and direction finding stations, FPBs kept radio silence in transit. Searching for the enemy was difficult. It required precise navigation and wide strips to be searched. In consequence, many missions were abortive. The probability of success increased when accurate radio intelligence became available, provided that it was possible to get it to the FPBs without delay. In direct encounters with the enemy, the advantage lay with the Germans. Their low silhouette made discrimination of the German boats difficult, and the gunfire of destroyers was successfully dodged by means of high speed and agility.

As radar was introduced on the British side, the success of the German FPBs declined markedly. Aircraft were capable of locating them, and even if they were not able to launch an attack they could at least report their positions. Radar stations, too, were able to give early warning. Before the MGBs themselves were equipped with radar, shore-based stations guided them to the enemy. When destroyers and later on MGBs in their turn were equipped with radar, this kind of control was effectively continued, since it allowed MGBs to keep radio silence.

The Germans were unable to catch up with the technical lead of the British. A German radar designed for small boats never reached operational status. The acquisition capabilities of radar warning receivers, today's ESM equipment, did not keep pace with the technological improvement of the radars.

Like the British, the German FPBs found that MGBs came to be their principal opponents. While the British had taken the initiative and revised their concept, deliberately pitting FPBs against FPBs in battle, the Germans were forced to accept this situation. Their proper targets were the supply ships. But frequently these could only be attacked when the units protecting them, most of them FPBs, had been eliminated. In addition, their transit and return were interfered with by encounters with enemy FPBs. Although the requirement 'the objective of FPB operations is attack upon convoys; escorts and defence forces will be avoided'[13] remained valid, this requirement was seldom met in the course of operations.

The necessity of coming to grips with equivalent units that were not the targets of the operation should have had implications for the operational tactics and armament of the German FPBs. But there was no decisive change in operational tactics owing to the fact that the Germans failed to identify the cause of the encounters correctly—the radar detection capability of the British MGBs.[14] Therefore, the only action taken was to equip the German FPBs with heavier guns which were to enable them to defeat the MGBs. Thus the original armament of light guns designed to protect the boats against equivalent opponents in cases of unintentional, accidental encounters was replaced by heavier guns which permitted them to defeat enemy FPBs in a dogfight.

17

Postwar Developments in FPB Warfare

For operations in offshore waters or peripheral seas, the Federal Republic of Germany and Denmark, both bordering on the Baltic, retained strong FPB components of their navies as partners in the North Atlantic Alliance, in spite of the postwar change in geostrategic conditions. But as the technology and armament of the first postwar generation of FPBs remained largely the same as those of their predecessors, such conceptual changes as were first identifiable were confined to the tactics of torpedo employment. No change in operational concepts was effected until the transition from the generation of torpedo FPBs to missile carriers and the leap in technology taken when FPBs were fitted with Naval Tactical Data Systems (NIDS) incorporating *LINK 11* and the latest in technology.

Today the FPB, although increased in tonnage to corvette size, is still a small weapon platform in comparison with destroyers and frigates. It continues to be the ideal naval weapon system for peripheral seas, maritime areas of archipelago structure and offshore waters. Although it continues to lack all-weather capability, its employment in peripheral seas such as the Baltic or in offshore waters is only impeded for a few days per annum.

FPB endurance, too, continues to be limited and essentially dependent on the physical endurance of the crew. On the other hand, modern weapon technology and miniaturisation in electronics make the modern FPB a match even for any larger class of warship. Today, all weapons, sensors, Naval Tactical Data Systems and electronic warfare systems usually carried by larger units are also available on board FPBs.

BALTIC OPERATIONS

The postwar geostrategic situation, characterised by cold war and the antagonism of the two superpowers and their respective alliances, made the Federal Republic of Germany and Denmark, the two NATO countries bordering on the Baltic, concentrate early on the peripheral seas—the Baltic, the Baltic Approaches and the North Sea.

In the phase of maritime arms buildup initiated by the Soviet Union and its partners in the Warsaw Pact, the Baltic where the Pact controlled more than 1500 kilometres of coastline retained its paramount importance for shipbuilding, training, logistics, maritime infrastructure and not least for naval operations. On the one hand, the Baltic with more than 20 ports that are used or usable for military purposes was and is the ideal base and line of communication for strategic operations against NATO's Atlantic lifelines and would have lent itself equally well as a joint warfare scenario where naval forces, combined with ground and air forces could be concentrated to outflank the European key region of Central Europe and to cut off NATO's Northern European Command from Central Europe. Under these aspects Copenhagen was regarded as the most heavily exposed capital of a NATO partner.

On the other hand, the German and Danish naval and naval air forces in NATO's Baltic Approaches Command control the waters around the Jutland peninsula and the Danish archipelago, so that from Moscow's point of view the Baltic Approaches were plugged up. Over the years, the Soviet Union together with the Warsaw Pact built up a considerable peripheral sea potential in the Baltic comprising a total of about 1600 units. Four key elements were distinguishable:

▶ First, an efficient amphibious force which would suffice to land more than 6000 fully equipped combat troops at one go in the first wave of an amphibious assault. With more than 100 amphibious units ranging from large landing ships to modern hovercraft over 50 per cent of the WP amphibious forces were deployed in the Baltic. Modernisation of the amphibious component by deploying new landing craft continued well into the Gorbachev era.

▶ Second, a multitude of efficient small surface combatants from FPBs to corvettes. *Osa*, the first actually operational missile FPB, is the typical combatant in the Baltic, and her hull which is almost identical with that of the torpedo carrier *Shershen* gives evidence of the transition from torpedo carrier to missile FPB. With their great number of light and medium combatants the Soviets achieved the sustainability *vis-à-vis* NATO forces required to secure the use of the Baltic by their own maritime forces.

▶ Third, sizable mine countermeasures units and stocks of mines in depots which defy any exact estimate. The Soviet Union delegated responsibility for mine countermeasures and mine warfare as one of the main tasks of the satellite navies: they were tasked to counter the mine warfare NATO was expected to conduct with the object of barring the Baltic Approaches.

▶ And fourth, the necessity of maintaining sizable ASW forces in the Baltic to eliminate the NATO submarine threat operating in the Baltic right off their own coasts; a threat not only to amphibious forces but also to the naval forces entering or leaving the Baltic.

From the beginning, and specifically since the adoption of the concepts of Flexible Response and Forward Defence, NATO built up a posture of differentiated structure to oppose that WP naval presence. FPBs have always played a central part in that posture, for 40 German and about 10 Danish FPBs have been available in the area on a permanent basis and have moreover been practising joint operations in exercises, including co-operation with Norwegian FPBs, and the skill of taking advantage of the geographical features of the Norwegian coast.

Although the 50s and 60s were decades devoted to practising multinational co-operation between FPB forces, co-operation between FPBs and other naval or naval air forces did not really develop during those decades.

TORPEDO TACTICS

The operational concepts for FPBs concentrated on the effective use of the Second World War torpedo with its short range against amphibious forces or surface forces. Tactics of co-ordinated deployment for launching various types of spread salvo were developed, as were tactics of simultaneous attack from various—up to six—sectors. In FPB operations it is mandatory to compensate for the essential weaknesses of one's own main weapon, the torpedo, and to optimise survivability in a combat situation in which the FPB has to penetrate deep inside the effective range of the enemy weapons to a point at which its torpedoes can be launched.

The torpedo salvos co-ordinated by the launching FPBs are designed to deprive the target of any chance of dodging. In whatever way the enemy may try to evade the attack, be it by turning away or by closing in, or by speeding up or by going on as before, he is to be hit by at least one torpedo. Weapon expenditure for this tactic is almost intolerably high, but no other way of achieving an acceptable hit probability has been found.

Survivability of FPBs is increased by one or more groups of FPBs attacking simultaneously from various sectors. Although the FPB has to close with the enemy under his defensive fire, high speed reduces the period spent within the range of the enemy's weapons, while attacks from various sectors oblige the enemy to split up his defence, thus reducing its effectiveness.

Otherwise, the principle of 'the most difficult opponent of any FPB is an enemy FPB' was upheld. Therefore, one's own forces should be so deployed that encounters with enemy FPBs are possibly avoided to prevent early attrition, for under the principle 'FPBs, not gun boats', dogfights with enemy FPBs should only be accepted if they are inevitable.

FPB SQUADRONS

From the beginning, the Federal German Navy organised its FPB forces in squadrons of 10 FPBs each. Of these there were originally five and later four.

The operational concepts described above require operating in two-ship formations, groups or divisions. The usual procedure is the deployment of a squadron in two divisions of five FPBs each with the squadron commander in command of the first division and his deputy in command of the second, operating on the basis of the common tactical concept.

FPB SUPPORT

Operational autonomy is to be reached by a technical concept optimised for FPB operations. The German FPBs have relied from the start on support afloat. Each of its 4 FPB squadrons has one organic tender of about 3000 tons

PLATE 17.1   A view from the open bridge of one of a squadron of German *Jaguar*
FPBs operating in the early 1960s. (*Photo: German Navy*)

displacement. In addition, a supply vessel is assigned to each squadron, responsible for the echelons of supply between depot level and Rear Combat Zone in offshore waters. While the FPBs are operating, the tender is replenished in protected rear areas. Upon their return from their missions, the FPBs meet their tender at a pre-arranged Coastal Supply Point (CSP) and go alongside for rest, resupply, refuel and maintenance.

This technical-logistic concept makes for operational flexibility. It ensures independence from shore-based resupply facilities. And, providing a capability for rapid redeployment from one geographical area to another, it extends the limited operational endurance of the one-watch boats indefinitely.

When the new generation of 'system-supported' missile FPBs was introduced in the mid-70s, the technical-logistic concept was further refined and adapted to the requirements associated with new technologies: 'Centralised maintenance' and 'preventive repair' are the new key words aimed at ensuring the physical operational readiness of the vessels under changed conditions as well. FPBs are not capable of storing spare parts and electronic modules in adequate quantities on board ship, nor have the members of the crew, as users of the system, the skills required to keep it in good repair. In consequence, a Centralised Maintenance Group holding extensive stocks of spare parts, similar to those for flying units, will be based on the tender.

FPBs returning from missions will hand over their repair and maintenance requests, based on a software-controlled internal diagnosis, to the group of skilled technicians and specialists who will check and restore the FPBs' physical readiness during the crews' period of rest at the CSP.

For long years, combat aircraft of the first postwar generations did not have a night fighting capability. In consequence, FPBs became a night fighting organisation in order to evade the air threat in offshore waters of peripheral seas. At nightfall they left the CSP for night operations. At dawn they were to be back inside their own NATO Integrated Air Defence Zone. The daylight hours were used as a phase of rest and preparations for the following night's operation.

PLATE 17.2 The German FPB tender *Main*, commissioned in 1963, acts as the
Depot ship to the 5th FPB Squadron. (*Photo: German Navy*)

In those days, the tender, with its comparatively powerful anti-aircraft weapons
and, for the time, modern fire control equipment, had also the task of providing
terminal protection against aircraft attack to the FPBs and their crews resting at
the anchorage.

The development of aircraft equipped with stand-off weapons and having an
all-weather fighting capability has long since turned night into day for operational
purposes. It will be shown below that although this has not made support afloat
based on the tender concept obsolete, other conceptual and operational measures
have had to be taken to ensure survivability of FPBs and tenders in action and in
the Rear Area at the CSP.

THE LONG-RANGE WIRE-GUIDED TORPEDO

The Danes claim to have produced the first wire-guided torpedo after World
War II, a 1950s adaptation of the German *Type G7a*. In the 1960s came the long-
range wire-guided torpedo. Several nations had begun earlier to make experiments aimed at overcoming the torpedo dilemma of a hit probability that was
much too low. A model that has become widely known, *inter alia* as an export
weapon, is the Swedish *Type 61* which, although of comparatively simple design,
still permits the torpedo to be influenced after being launched.

On the German side, in contrast, the development of the *Sea Eel* torpedo family
took much longer, with the result that a highly intelligent weapon system was
finally introduced—a torpedo capable of being used in the anti-surface role by
submarines as well as by FPBs.

The fundamentals of wire-guided torpedo technology were explained above.
The first FPBs of the Federal German Navy which were fitted with this weapon
also benefited from the modern computerised fire control system associated with
it. As a result, the boats so equipped had no longer to close with the enemy to the
shortest possible range but were able to concentrate on launching their torpedoes

at long range at the approaching enemy from waiting positions providing the maximum possible protection or camouflage.

This reduced the FPBs' own risk markedly, for the introduction of the combined fire control system also provided radar and optical fire control to their guns, too. Thus, FPBs acquired a night fighting capability for their guns as well and were enabled effectively to defend themselves against the growing air threat.

Since the intelligent wire-guided torpedo with a single-round hit probability, which surpasses that of missiles, has become available, torpedo employment of course no longer requires group operations, let alone the commitment of a full division. The number of closely linked FPBs has therefore been reduced to two- or three-ship formations operating on the basis of a common formation concept. The underlying reason for this decision was to have them proceed together in the transit phases during which two or three FPBs would optimise their air defence through mutual support.

In view of the target density to be expected in the area of operations, it had also to be borne in mind that each FPB now carried no more than two torpedoes. Carrying reload torpedoes is out of the question as the sensitive torpedo electronics would have been destroyed by hull vibrations outside the tubes that rested on anti-vibration mountings. FPBs being equipped with these torpedoes have also had to sacrifice their former fast minelaying capability because of the special mountings of the torpedo tubes.

Although it is true that one single shot can be expected to have a destructive effect on a target, the target density in the area of operations and the growing air threat make at least group deployments appear sensible. In practice, deployment

PLATE 17.3 A squadron of German *Type 148/Tiger* class FPBs at sea, led by the *Panther*. This class carries a 76 mm OTO-Melara gun forward and *four* Exocet missiles aft. (*Photo: German Navy*)

to individual waiting/laying-up positions will anyway be determined by geography and the missions concerned.

In contrast with earlier days, the speed of the vessels has assumed an entirely new importance since the introduction of the wire-guided torpedo. For the purpose of assuring the vessels' own survivability during the phase of penetration into the enemy's reach, speed is hardly required any more. What speed ensures nowadays is FPB flexibility and versatility as an all-round asset and an instrument of crisis management: today, surveillance in the central and eastern Baltic; tomorrow in turn patrol or naval presence in the Skagerrak or in the North Sea. In between, resupply/rest at the CSP in the Rear Area. Speed can also ensure that one's own units will arrive at the area of operations earlier than the enemy's, an advantage whose tactical benefit can be decisive.

PLATE 17.4   The German FPB *Geier* of the 1976 *Type 143* class testing its defensive sprinkler system against nuclear/biological/chemical attack. (*Photo: German Navy*)

PLATE 17.5   Steel-hulled FPBs started to appear in the early 1970s. This is the lead ship of the Royal Norwegian Navy's *Snogg* class. (*Photo: Royal Norwegian Navy*)

FPBs AS MINELAYERS

Moreover, speed continues to be essential for minelaying operations: Of the 40 missile FPBs of the Federal German Navy only 10 units in the 2nd FPB Squadron are still equipped with the modern wire-guided torpedo. As for the other 30 vessels, it was decided to abandon the torpedo component in order to maintain an assured capability for fast minelaying.

The requirement for fast minelaying is an integral part of the operational concept for the naval forces of the Atlantic Alliance in the Baltic Approaches (BALTAP) Command. FPBs are capable of barring critical straits at short notice. They are also capable of reinforcing minefields at short notice and under the cover of darkness, even in a threat environment in waters where the enemy is already present. And they can execute raid-type offensive minelaying operations in enemy waters. Thus, as we have already noted, speed continues to be essential for FPBs under the current operational concepts. Nowadays, however, it is not so much a fighting capability but rather a condition for flexibility and versatility.

COMBINED OPERATIONS

This brings us, if not to the present, then at least to the latest leap in techno-logical development characterising the modern FPB as a 'missile platform, NTDS (*LINK 11*)-fitted and with sophisticated hard kill and soft kill capabilities in elec-tronic warfare'—a 'mini destroyer with reduced endurance'. It is obvious that for these surface combatants whose complexity as a weapon system makes the desig-nation FPB seem rather quaint, operational and tactical concepts had to be revised as well.

Today, the speed, size and equipment of such vessels enable them by means of force concentration effectively to prevail even over larger units and even in the open sea, albeit for limited periods, and to gain geographically limited or tempo-rary superiority. On the other hand, peripheral seas and offshore waters have long since come to be the scene of the extremely complex conduct of operations where a wide variety of naval assets, including shore-based elements and naval air forces, perform their tasks. The complexity of the scenario in the coastal zone, which even in the event of armed conflict requires consideration of neutral shipping, fisheries and trade, has put an end to concepts of autonomous, type-oriented operations in these areas. This applies to FPBs as much as to any other naval weapon system.

The operational concept of the NATO navies in the Baltic and Baltic Approaches as repeatedly described in German White Papers on defence since the mid-70s may serve as an example.

In this area, where geographical and oceanographical factors dictate the inter-linking of land, air and naval warfare planning in a joint scenario, the operational concept seeks to ensure 'presence', surveillance and deterrence in peace; control and crisis management in crisis, and defence in depth in war.

Defence in depth is a sound objective of the Atlantic Alliance, not only in peripheral seas and offshore waters but also in the open sea up to and well into the northern Norwegian Sea for the purpose of protecting the Atlantic lifelines, and calls for the coordinated employment of all available naval assets.

Employment of FPBs alone is no longer conceivable. Employment of helicopters not only in a support role as remote sensor platforms but also for the exploitation of weapon ranges in third party targeting (TPT) is as much a matter of course as is the employment of fighter bombers in an escort role—so as to pose a multi-threat with a view to increasing the sustainability and survivability of one's own forces.

Direct co-operation of different naval weapon systems is not actually required and frequently not even desired. Availability of a comprehensive real-time situation plot which the Maritime Headquarters (MHQ) provides via links to the units at sea makes the burden of co-ordination among the units in the area of operation superfluous. Each unit can concentrate on its mission with the utmost autonomy. In spite of a highly dispersed deployment and breaking up of the close proximity of units to each other in former FPB formations, operations continue to be governed by the common tactical concept, and this is ensured by 'control by veto' through the officer in tactical command of the formation. Under the conceptual umbrella of an MHQ which acts as the centre of co-ordination, providing in particular for integration with the air defence organisation and additional assets such as NATO *E3A AWACS*, each individual FPB is a unit operating autonomously on the basis of the common concept of the formation. In the conduct of operations, the modern FPB as a missile-carrying platform is an integral part of the overall system, comprising MHQ and the other naval and naval air forces.

18

Coastal Operations: The Future

As we have seen, the commercial, political and strategic importance of coastal waters has grown in recent years and is likely to continue to do so. This has been reflected in the extension of the sea areas in which nations have needed to supervise, in the shape both of larger territorial seas and the new 200-mile Exclusive Economic Zones. As the areas of jurisdiction have expanded, so have the number of navies with a physical capacity to conduct the necessary supervision. In the future, therefore, coastal operations of all sorts are more likely to grow than to decline in importance. This leads to a great many questions. How, in general, will technology affect the conduct of coastal operations? Will naval planners be looking for single or multipurpose coastal vessels? How will they interact with conventional bluewater naval forces? In this last chapter we try to grapple with some of these issues.

OFFSHORE PATROL

Because modern requirements have made the offshore tapestry so important, the world's navies will have many coastal tasks to perform, both in peace and in war. Table 18: 1 attempts to define the resultant tasks of the OPV against the requirements.

Shipbuilders in the UK have produced various designs for export which have sprung from the concept of the OPV3. These include Vosper Thorneycroft's *Vigilance* class. This design has a speed above 30 knots and a range of 5500nm at 12 knots, a 76mm gun, surface to surface missiles, chaff and flares for self protection, a helicopter deck, spare additional accommodation for 24 persons and 2 fast inflatable boats. A crew of 50 reflects the needs of the weapon fit. Such a vessel lacks only anti-submarine sensors and weapons, but such an addition would also require extensive noise reduction to be effective in this role and hence turn the OPV design into a frigate.

Looking further into the future, a surface effect hull has been envisaged for an OPV design. This type of hull would provide a more stable platform in heavy weather and greater speed than that obtainable from the traditional hull. The only surface effect hulls of this size in service are large ferries which have been lightly constructed. An OPV must carry weapons and be reasonably robust. Whilst having advantages over the traditional design, a surface effect solution for the OPV requirement is therefore likely to be an expensive vessel when compared with a traditional hull solution.

The development of the OPV is pushing it further towards the type of vessel more traditionally called a frigate. However, most OPV hulls are designed on the lines of their commercial counterpart rather than on the sophisticated requirements of a frigate's hull. In deciding whether an OPV or a 'mini frigate' or a corvette is required for offshore patrol work, the likely tasks and any threats should be established. The requirements of the vessel can then be decided. Many coastal areas do not have a submarine threat, but should there be one this will be a major factor in the choice of vessel. A hull with sonar fitted requires a quietness that is not found in the traditional OPV hull. A submarine threat therefore normally leads to the more expensive 'mini frigate' solution. The only alternative, but less effective, solution is an OPV capable of controlling a self-contained anti-submarine helicopter. The helicopter could be based ashore, refuelling as necessary from the OPV, or onboard the OPV.

Airships have been put forward as a cost effective method of carrying out the OPV's task. The need for OPVs in addition to aircraft has already been explained. But the airship does not suffer from the need to maintain the high speed which a fixed-wing aircraft requires. An airship has already demonstrated that it can place an inflatable boat in the water, although it has not demonstrated the recovery of the boat. There are possibilities in the offshore tapestry for the airship, but it is the equivalent of the policeman in his panda car, rather than the policeman on the beat. For this reason it is unlikely to replace the OPV on permanent patrol in its area.

MINE WARFARE

What of the future for Mine Warfare? In previous chapters we have already considered a number of more recent developments, some of which have yet to enter operational service. This section summarises these and other, less immediate, prospects.

Mining will continue to develop, with 'guardian' mines to protect minefields from specific MCM attack. With increasing weapon mobility, another possibility is the use of a sensor field with a remote, well concealed weapon battery, which could comprise just a few highly sophisticated weapons, with the sensors deployed over a much greater area and very much more difficult to detect. Of perhaps greater impact, however, will be the evolution of more advanced means of target detection. A number of possibilities have been considered, including the local disturbance of the earth's gravitational field, variations in electric potential, seismic distrubance and the shadows from natural background noise, the sun's rays or even cosmic rays. These effects, any of which may be caused by a potential mine target, will present major difficulties to platform designers in terms of signature reduction, but are of such low magnitude compared to those currently used that a considerable investment in research will be needed before any practical systems could be deployed.

As far as MCM is concerned, minesweeping may be due for something of a renaissance, with the arrival of the Variable Moment Magnet (VMM), and the realisation of the target sweeping concept, although given the existing worldwide stocks of older, simpler mines, there will continue to be a place for the traditional approach.

	Good damage control system	Degaussing	Good navigation equipment	Good position-recording equipment	Military radio equipment	Commercial radio equipment	Reasonable ship speed	Good fuel and water capacity	Good sea-keeping ability	High speed inflatable boat	Gun	Surface missiles	Anti-air missiles	Good surface radar	Air warning radar	Helicopter capable	Towed side scan sonar	Divers and diving equipment	Oil disposal equipment	Good medical outfit	Additional portable fire-fighting equipment	Additional food stocks	Spare accommodation	Flood fighting	Shipped scrambling nets	Dress ship flags	Warship appearance
PERIOD																											
Policeman on the beat			✓			✓	✓	✓	✓					✓				✓	✓	✓							✓
Co-operation with military aircraft			✓	✓	✓		✓	✓	✓					✓	✓												
Co-operation with civil aircraft			✓	✓		✓	✓	✓	✓					✓													
Immigration control	✓		✓	✓		✓		✓	✓	✓				✓					✓	✓							✓
Anti terrorist patrols	✓		✓	✓	✓	✓	✓	✓	✓	✓				✓		✓		✓	✓	✓					✓	✓	✓
Oil rig protection	✓		✓	✓	✓	✓	✓	✓	✓	✓				✓		✓		✓	✓	✓					✓	✓	✓
Fishery protection/enforcement	✓		✓	✓	✓	✓	✓	✓	✓	✓				✓		✓		✓	✓	✓					✓	✓	✓
Anti pirate patrols	✓		✓	✓	✓	✓	✓	✓	✓	✓				✓											✓	✓	✓
Anti smuggling patrols	✓		✓	✓	✓	✓	✓	✓	✓	✓				✓													✓
Drug surveillance	✓		✓	✓	✓	✓	✓	✓	✓	✓				✓					✓								✓
Yacht race escort						✓		✓	✓																		
'Showing the Flag'	✓		✓			✓	✓	✓	✓	✓	✓			✓								✓	✓	✓	✓	✓	✓
Naval recruiting	✓		✓			✓		✓	✓	✓	✓											✓	✓	✓	✓	✓	✓
PERIOD OF RISING TENSION																											
Anti infiltration patrols	✓		✓	✓	✓		✓	✓	✓	✓	✓			✓		✓			✓								
Surveillance	✓		✓	✓	✓		✓	✓	✓	✓	✓			✓		✓	✓	✓	✓								
Marking	✓		✓	✓	✓			✓	✓					✓			✓	✓									
Route Survey	✓	✓	✓	✓	✓			✓	✓					✓		✓	✓										
Air Picket	✓		✓	✓	✓			✓	✓			✓	✓	✓	✓				✓	✓							✓
Coastal convoy administrative escort	✓	✓	✓	✓	✓		✓	✓	✓		✓			✓		✓											
WAR																											
Minefield gate patrol	✓	✓	✓	✓	✓		✓	✓	✓	✓	✓			✓		✓											
Minesweeper/hunter support	✓	✓	✓	✓	✓		✓	✓	✓		✓			✓					✓	✓							
Despatch vessel	✓		✓		✓		✓	✓	✓	✓										✓							
Landing on occupied coastlines	✓	✓	✓	✓	✓			✓	✓	✓	✓			✓		✓			✓	✓							
Warfare in shallow waters	✓	✓	✓	✓	✓		✓	✓	✓	✓	✓	✓	✓	✓						✓							✓

FIG. 18.1 Requirements for an OPV

PLATE 18.1 *Vigilance.* A Future OPV Design (*Photo: Vosper Thorneycroft*)

PLATE 18.2   A Surface Effect Hull OPV Design (*Photo: Vosper Thorneycroft*)

In minehunting, on the other hand, aside from ongoing improvements in the technology of existing systems, a somewhat more innovative technique is starting to gain
favour, as a means of dealing with the more sophisticated mines, with effective
ranges well in excess of those of the minehunting sonars currently available to
detect and classify them. By putting the sonar in an ROV, it can be deployed close
enough to the minefield to carry out its purpose, while the vehicle is actually
controlled from a much safer distance, perhaps as much as two kilometres away.
This has the further advantage that the operating platform need not be a specialised,
and expensive, purpose-built MCM vessel, but could be any platform, even the lead
vessel of a convoy, on which the requisite control facilities can be deployed.
Examples of ROVs designed for this type of operation are the Ferranti *MANTA*,
and the Plessey, now Marconi, ARMS (Advanced Remote Minehunting System)
illustrated in Figs 18.2 and 18.3 and Plate 18.3. ARMS is of further interest in that
it uses a new type of sonar incorporating an acoustic mirror.

Navigational techniques have improved dramatically over the years, and particularly with the availability of accurate positional information from Navstar/
GPS. The somewhat more radical approach of bottom contour profiling is a possible acoustic technique, whereby the sea-bed contours are measured by an echo
sounder and compared with known, previously measured profiles in order to
determine position. This requires considerable data processing power, and is still
rather in its infancy, but it may well prove viable for certain types of operation.
Following on from this is the question of electronic charts, which are now a reality,
at least technically, but have yet to realise much of their significant operational
potential. Although it may be many years before general navigation and ship's
safety are entrusted to such technology, there must surely be a place for effective
and comprehensive electronic storage and display of geographical information
in many naval endeavours, including mine warfare, where vast quantities of
such data have to be handled and transferred, as yet unsupported by common
standards or formats. Indeed, the whole business of managing route survey and
related data lags well behind other areas of development and requires much
greater prominence in ongoing MCM programmes.

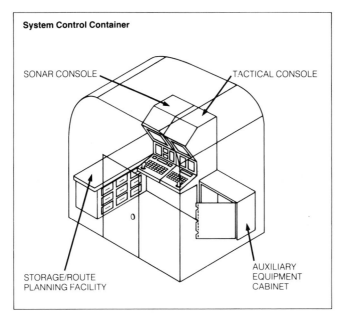

FIG. 18.2   *Advanced Remote Minehunting System* (ARMS)—containerised layout
(*Marconi*)

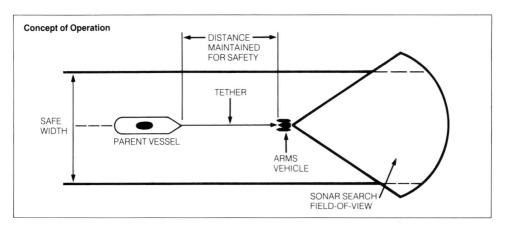

FIG. 18.3   ARMS—Concept of Operation (*Marconi.*)

The developments outlined above should serve to provide a flavour of the opportunities offered by advances in technology, but many of them may never be realised. It seems inevitable that the balance will continue to lie in favour of mines rather than the countermeasures. Despite the significant, if not decisive, impact it can have on almost any naval operation, as the numerous examples from history make only too clear, to many navies, mine warfare has always been, and probably always will be, the poor relation, far from the top of the priority list for procurement and resources, and starved of funding in favour of other, often

PLATE 18.3 *The Advanced Remote Minehunting System* (ARMS). The complete system can be supplied in three containers, one of which is used to provide the control facilities. (*Photo: Marconi*)

more glamorous, projects. In a branch of warfare so deeply founded on the laws of probability, there is one enduring certainty, which is that navies will never have enough of the resources they really need to match the threat posed by mines.

FAST PATROL BOATS

In the light of technological developments, FPBs are no longer FPBs as they were once understood. The small fighting vessel of past years has long since outgrown its initial order of magnitude and has become a multipurpose platform of medium size which may well be designated as a fast corvette.

Although sustained operations in the open sea, such as protecting NATO's lifelines across the Atlantic, cannot be assigned to such units, FPB construction is experiencing a definite boom in global terms—in Europe as well as in the Middle East, Africa and South America—with differing approaches to further development; this is due to a number of factors. An obvious reason, of course, is the lack of funds in small and medium-sized countries. Considering that FPBs have a combat power comparable to that of far larger units and that naval shipbuilding costs are increasing by leaps and bounds, FPBs must be regarded as extremely cost-effective. In addition, there is the fact that, especially in the recent past, interest has focused on peripheral seas and coastal zones which have come to be a scene of frequent conflicts. It is not in the mid-Atlantic that the freedom of the seas and world trade are exposed to risks, but rather in straits, peripheral seas and coastal zones.

The events witnessed during the conflict between Iran and Iraq and the resultant problems of protecting international shipping in the Strait of Hormuz are an example in point of how difficult it is for the great navies with Atlantic units to control offshore waters; all too frequently, coastal states with modern FPBs manage to avoid patrolling naval forces and succeed in interfering with merchant ships.

With the exception of the Falklands war, which was in a category all by itself, situations of crisis and conflict of the recent past have had the characteristics of regional crises and regional conflicts that bore witness both to the extremely high risk to which large combatants are exposed in offshore waters and to the flexibility and effectiveness of the FPB which now should be more fittingly designated as a 'small surface combatant'.

To be sure, aircraft carriers are an excellent instrument of power projection. But these units are effectively available to and, above all, affordable for the super-powers alone. For small and medium-size coastal states, on the other hand, the FPB has turned out to be the ideal instrument of crisis management. These small but extremely combat effective units permit control of a maritime area to be gained and maintained effectively. Control, surveillance and the capability for swift concentration of combat power, maybe by surprise, are the foundations of successful crisis management. FPBs can on the contrary also be used to take escalating action by short surprise raids which can shatter the superior position of an opponent temporarily or permanently.

So it is not at all surprising that primarily small and medium-size countries are the main buyers ordering FPB new construction. This applies especially to the

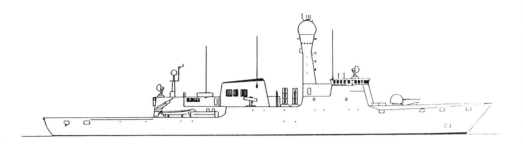

Fig. 18.4   The Danish *Thetis* light frigate

countries bordering on the choke points of the world shipping lanes of which the Baltic with the Baltic Approaches is but one example of many. One need not be much of a prophet to predict that protection of the Atlantic lifelines will undoubtedly remain the key task of the Atlantic Alliance, a task for which the NATO navies have effectively prepared themselves. On the other hand, however, it is equally evident that protection of shipping in the straits and coastal zones in the area of operations of small and fast combatants is growing more and more difficult.

How the technology of such combatants is developing can be observed at the shipbuilders' fitting-out piers. Today, FPBs are reaching the 600-ton mark. Data links such as *LINK 11* in German FPBs are still an exception, but in addition to armament comprising most modern missiles for anti-ship missile defence (ASMD), many FPBs can now operate helicopters, or at least ship-based drones, for the purpose of extending their detection horizon.

Against this background it is particularly interesting to look at Danish experience. Since the early 1980s, the Royal Danish Navy has had to cope with having regularly to replace a high proportion of its ships. In 1991, for example, it reported that some 30 of its ships would need to be scrapped by the mid 1990s, leaving only about 26 real warships in the fleet. At the same time, the end of the Cold War had created an expectation of a peace dividend which would make a one-for-one replacement completely impossible. But it was clear to the Danish authorities that they would continue to have real and demanding tasks in their own complicated and important waters. The Danes have come up with a number of interesting responses to this fundamental and all too common dilemma. Their overall aim is to create an 'Economy Navy' of flexible, highly automated ships that can be sailed by very small crews with minimum upkeep costs.

The cost effectiveness of the Navy is to be improved by providing ships with additional civilian roles, making naval forces better value for money. The Danes are looking at the idea of making naval vessels available, at a price, for a number of other tasks in support of Government agencies, such as:

▶ Surveying

▶ Oceanography

▶ Buoy Tender Work

▶ Fishery Protection

▶ Environmental Protection

▶ Sea Traffic Control

▶ Scientific Research.

For example, they have recently launched the *Thetis*-class of lightly armed fishery protection frigates. At 2600 tons, *Thetis* is a large ship, but this is explained by its need to operate in the difficult waters around Greenland. It is also expected to be heavily involved in a seismological survey of Greenland's coastal waters for the next few years.

Thetis is also significant for the fact that it takes the idea of modularity in ship design one step further. As a private venture, one Danish yard is investigating the idea of producing a much more heavily armed version of the *Thetis* class, with provision for the fitting of the Oto Melara 76 mm gun, *Seasparrow*, a Close-in Weapons System (CIWS) and *Harpoon*. Its access to a range of modularised weapon and sensor systems means that *Thetis* can be 're-roled' in a month. Many of its systems are also interchangeable with those of the even more interesting 'Standard Flex 300' concept. The idea behind this concept is to use a GRP hull as the platform for a variety of weapons and sensors which can be easily exchanged as the need arises. The ship can be fitted for a number of roles, namely peacetime surveillance, minewarfare, FPB operations, ASW and environmental. At 54 metres and 450 tons, this scheme is therefore a good example of the future potentiality of the large FPB or Corvette.

In theory, it should take the vessel less than 12 hours to shift from one role to another, including the exchange of up to four containers, loading of new supplies, ammunition and missiles and the input of new software. First orders were placed in 1985 and the whole programme of 16 ships is expected to complete in 1997.[1] This innovative approach to the problem of combining flexibility with the utmost economy will be watched closely by other navies. But it is really too soon to tell whether it will be possible to combine FPB and minewarfare tasks in so small a ship and whether it will be possible to train one crew for such widely different activities.

Irrespective of its success, however, the adventurous Standard Flex programme confirms the internationally discernible trend of small and medium-size navies towards the introduction of versatile units optimised for operations in offshore waters, straits and peripheral seas. When cost, size, equipment and combat power are considered, two points emerge: first, the FPB in her original form as a small fighting vessel for hit-and-run operations is outdated. Secondly, the FPB as a sustainable and combat effective surface combat platform approximating to corvette size is experiencing a boom at the moment—especially when working with naval air forces—and holds considerable prospects for the future. The

PLATE 18.4 The Danish *Standard Flex 300* is a 450 ton FPB/Corvette capable of a variety of coastal roles. Also indicative of a new future is that it is here shown operating with a helicopter from the former East German Navy. (*Photo: Lt Cdr Stehr.*)

ATTACK ROLE

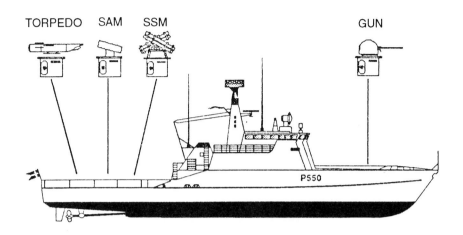

TORPEDO   SAM   SSM   GUN

FIG. 18.5   *Standard Flex* as an FPB

MCM ROLE

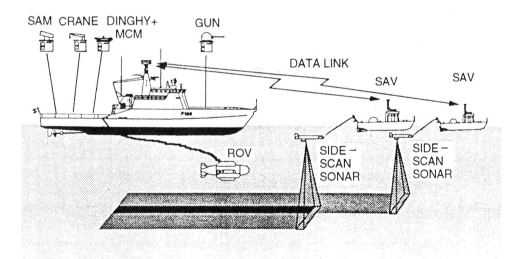

SAM CRANE DINGHY+   GUN
                MCM

DATA LINK

SAV   SAV

ROV

SIDE –   SIDE –
SCAN   SCAN
SONAR   SONAR

FIG. 18.6   *Standard Flex* as an MCM Ship

SURVEILLANCE ROLE

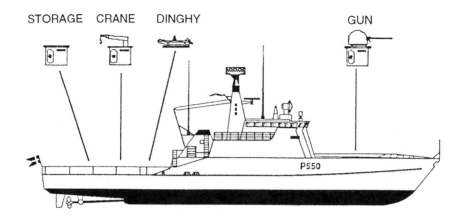

FIG. 18.7   *Standard Flex* in the Surveillance role

MINELAYING ROLE

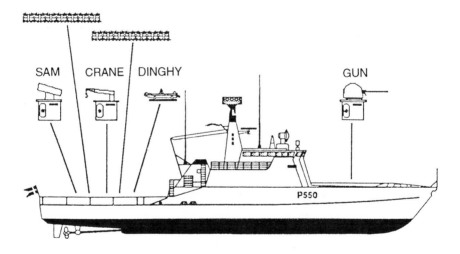

FIG. 18.8   *Standard Flex* in the Minelaying Role

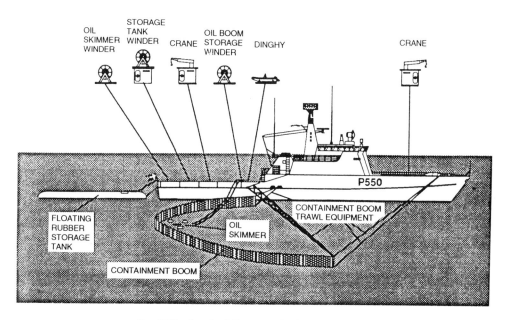

Fig. 18.9 *Standard Flex* as an Environmental Ship

FPB/Corvette's special qualifications both as a flexible instrument of crisis management and as a combat platform are probably equally responsible for this. And so is the growing importance of the area of operations for which the new FPBs are designed, namely coastal waters and peripheral seas where coastal states try to safeguard their interests, leaving the open oceans to the larger powers.

References

Chapter 1 • Maritime Operations in Coastal Waters

1. Rear-Adm. N.P. V'yunenko and others, The Navy: its Roles, Prospects for Development and Employment. Moscow: Military Publishing House, 1988.

Chapter 14 • Fast Patrol Boat Operations: An Introduction

1. Fock, H, Schnellboote, Vol. 4. Herford 1986, p. 4.
2. Meyers, Flottentaschenbuch 1989, Munich 1988.
3. Marriott, J, Fast Attack Craft, London 1978, p. 9.
4. Der Friedensvertrag, Charlottenburg 1919, p. 93.

Chapter 15 • The Technology of FPB Operations

1. Fock, H, op. cit., Vol. 4. Herford 1986, p. 14.
2. Meyers, Flottentaschenbuch 1982, Munich 1981, p. 647.
3. ibid.

Chapter 16 • Operational Concepts: FPB in the Second World War

1. Fock, H, op.cit., Vol. 1 Herford 1973, p. 71.
2. Fock, H, op.cit., Vol. 2. Herford 1974, p. 9.
3. Fock, H, op.cit., Vol. 1. Herford 1983, p. 81.
4. Giermann, C, Schnellbootseinsätze der Kriegsmarine, Führungsakademie der Bundeswehr, Hamburg 1970, p. 26.
5. ibid., p. 30.
6. Fock, H, op.cit., Vol. 1 Herford 1973, p. 132.
7. ibid., p. 149.
8. Giermann, C, op.cit., p. 8.
9. ibid.
10. ibld.
11. ibid.
12. ibid.
13. Frank, H, Editor, Die Schnellbootflottille, Flensburg 1984, p. 30.
14. Gierman, C, op.cit., p. 45a.

Chapter 18 • Coastal Operations: The Future

1. Information gained from a briefing by Commander Viggo Hansen at Wilhelmshafen on 5 July 1991 and from Rear Admiral IB Rodholm at the ATI European Naval Forecast Conference, London in June 1991.

Index